Contents

G000153592

List of resources   3
Introduction   4
How to use the CD-ROM   5

Moving and growing   PAGE 7
Notes on the CD-ROM resources   8
Notes on the photocopiable pages 12
Photocopiable pages   14

Habitats   PAGE 20
Notes on the CD-ROM resources   21
Notes on the photocopiable pages 27
Photocopiable pages   30

Keeping warm   PAGE 37
Notes on the CD-ROM resources   38
Notes on the photocopiable pages 41
Photocopiable pages   43

Solids and liquids   PAGE 50
Notes on the CD-ROM resources   51
Notes on the photocopiable pages 56
Photocopiable pages   59

Circuits and conductors   PAGE 69
Notes on the CD-ROM resources   70
Notes on the photocopiable pages 73
Photocopiable pages   75

Text © Carole Creary and Gay Wilson
© 2004 Scholastic Ltd

Published by Scholastic Ltd, Villiers House,
Clarendon Avenue, Leamington Spa,
Warwickshire CV32 5PR

Printed by Bell & Bain Ltd, Glasgow

234567890 567890123

British Library Cataloguing-in-Publication Data
A catalogue record for this book is available from
the British Library.

ISBN 0-439-98495-5

**Visit our website at
www.scholastic.co.uk**

CD Developed in association with
Footmark Media Ltd

Authors
Carole Creary and Gay Wilson

Editor
Christine Harvey

Assistant Editor
Joel Lane

Series Designer
Joy Monkhouse

Designer
Jan Patalong

Cover photographs
© Photodisc,
Ingram Publishing

Acknowledgements

The publishers wish to thank:
John Lyons for *My Praying Mantis* by John Lyons from *A Caribbean Dozen* edited by John Agard and Grace Nicholls © 1996, John Lyons (1996, Walker Books)

Extracts from the National Curriculum for England © Crown copyright material is reproduced with the permission of the Controller of HMSO and the Queen's Printer for Scotland.

Every effort has been made to trace copyright holders and the publishers apologise for any omissions.

List of resources on the CD-ROM

The page numbers refer to the teacher's notes provided in this book.

Moving and growing

Human skeleton, Pigeon skeleton, Fish skeleton,
Snake skeleton   8
Skull x-ray, Hand x-ray, Broken leg x-ray   9
Front view of muscles, Back view of muscles   9
Snail, Beetle, Butterfly   10
Video: Being a sportsman   11

Habitats

Horse chestnut tree, Grass, Daisies,
Dandelions, Wheat, Human, Seal, Salmon,
Eagle, Tortoise, Snake; Snail, Slug, Worm,
Fly, Starfish, Crab   21
Bee, Wasp, Spider, Beetle, Daisies, Dandelions   22
Natural pond, Grassy field, Woodland, Plant trough,
Hedge   23
Shield bug, Bracket fungus, Newt, Teasel   24
Vertical food chain, Horizontal food chains   25
Thrush, Urban fox, Blue tit, Butterfly, Slug   26
Predator and prey   27

Keeping warm

Thermos flask, Fridge-freezer, Electric fan,
Fishing boat with ice in hold   38
Saucepan cooking, Child in winter clothes,
Chicks under warming lamp, Water tank with jacket   39

Solids and liquids

Pouring cooking oil, Pouring golden syrup,
Pouring water, Pouring custard   51
House brick, Wood, Glass vase, Pebble,
Plastic sandals, Metal fork, Cotton wool, Heap of
sand, Heap of rice, Plasticine   52
Dunking a teabag, Dissolving salt, Melting fat,
Dissolving ice cubes, Sifting flour, Candle melting,
Chocolate melting   53
Molten steel   55

Circuits and conductors

Wiring diagrams   70
Electrical symbols   70
Standard wall light switch, Button switch on a fan,
Turn switch on a radio   71
Three-pin plug, Headphone connector, Extension lead,
Back of computer   72
Dangers of electricity   73

INTRODUCTION

This book and CD-ROM support the teaching and learning set out in the QCA Scheme of Work for science in Year 4. The CD provides a large bank of visual and oral resources. The book provides teacher's notes, background information, ideas for discussion and activities to accompany the CD resources, along with photocopiable pages to support the teaching. All have been specifically chosen to meet the requirements for resources listed in five of the six QCA units for Year 3. The unit on Friction has been omitted, since this is a very practical unit. Some additional resources and ideas have also been included to enable teachers to develop and broaden these areas of study if they wish. These include poems, stories, information sheets and sheets to help children clarify their thinking or record what they find out.

The resources and activities are not intended to provide a structure for teaching in themselves, but are designed to give a basis for discussion and activities that focus on the knowledge, skills and understanding required by the National Curriculum for science. Some of the ideas build on the National Curriculum requirements and help to broaden the children's experiences.

The children are encouraged to develop such skills as observing, questioning, sorting, sequencing, describing, finding out, speaking, listening, reading, writing and drawing.

Links with other subjects
Maths
Skills such as counting, measuring, matching, ordering and sequencing are essential to both science and maths. Many of the suggested activities require the children to use such skills. The children have the opportunity to practise other mathematical skills – for example, making nets for cubes in order to represent food chains three-dimensionally. Sorting is an important mathematical and science skill, and the children have many opportunities to practise it – for example, when sorting various solid substances according to whether or not they will dissolve in water.

Literacy
There are a number of close links between the topics covered in this book and work on literacy. The discussion activities contribute directly to the requirements for speaking and listening. The poems and information sheets could be used in shared reading during the Literacy Hour, or to provide a stimulus for shared, guided or independent writing. There is considerable opportunity for the children to develop their independent writing skills as they produce leaflets or diaries or write simple poems using the word cards. Pictures from the CD could be printed to stimulate independent writing or to illustrate it.

Art and design
Many of the activities suggested in the teacher's notes encourage the children to use art and design to extend their understanding of a particular concept. For example, they are encouraged to make close observations in order to produce detailed drawings of creatures found in the local environment. Similarly, one activity focuses on making models of creatures from reclaimed materials.

Design and technology
The children learn to foillow circuit diagrams in order to make working electrical circuits; they also design and draw their own circuits.

History
In the unit on 'Keeping warm', the children learn about how people kept things cold before the advent of refrigerators. The children are also encouraged to find out more about the history of how ice was harvested and used in the past.

ICT
The children are encouraged to use the Internet whenever possible to search for more information on the subjects they are studying.

HOW TO USE THE CD-ROM

Windows NT users

If you use Windows NT you may see the following error message: 'The procedure entry point Process32First could not be located in the dynamic link library KERNEL32.dll'. Click on **OK** and the CD will autorun with no further problems.

Setting up your computer for optimal use

On opening, the CD will alert you if changes are needed in order to operate the CD at its optimal use. There are three changes you may be advised to make:

Viewing resources at their maximum screen size

To see images at their maximum screen size, your screen display needs to be set to 800 x 600 pixels. In order to adjust your screen size you will need to **Quit** the program.

If using a PC, open the **Control Panel**. Select **Display** and then **Settings**. Adjust the **Desktop Area** to 800 x 600 pixels. Click on **OK** and then restart the program.

If using a Mac, from the **Apple** menu select **Control Panels** and then **Monitors** to adjust the screen size.

Adobe Acrobat Reader

To print high-quality versions of images and to view and print the photocopiable pages on the CD you need **Adobe Acrobat Reader** installed on your computer. If you do not have it installed already, a version is provided on the CD. To install this version **Quit** the 'Ready Resources' program.

If using a PC, right-click on the **Start** menu on your desktop and choose **Explore**. Click on the **+** sign to the left of the CD drive entitled 'Ready Resources' and open the folder called 'Acrobat Reader Installer'. Run the program contained in this folder to install **Adobe Acrobat Reader**.

If using a Mac, double click on the 'Ready Resources' icon on the desktop and on the 'Acrobat Reader Installer' folder. Run the program contained in this folder to install **Adobe Acrobat Reader**.

PLEASE NOTE: If you do not have **Adobe Acrobat Reader** installed, you will not be able to print high-quality versions of images, or to view or print photocopiable pages (although these are provided in the accompanying book and can be photocopied).

QuickTime

In order to view the videos and listen to the audio on this CD you will need to have **QuickTime version 5 or later** installed on your computer. If you do not have it installed already, or have an older version of **QuickTime**, the latest version is provided on the CD. If you choose to install this version, **Quit** the 'Ready Resources' program.

If using a PC, right-click on the **Start** menu on your desktop and choose **Explore**. Click on the **+** sign to the left of the CD drive that is entitled 'Ready Resources' and open the folder called 'QuickTime Installer'. Run the program contained in this folder to install **QuickTime**.

If using a Mac, double click on the 'Ready Resources' CD icon on the desktop and then on the 'Acrobat Reader Installer' folder. Run the program contained in this folder to install **QuickTime**.

PLEASE NOTE: If you do not have **QuickTime** installed you will be unable to view the films.

Menu screen

▶ Click on the **Resource Gallery** of your choice to view the resources available under that topic.
▶ Click on **Complete Resource Gallery** to view all the resources available on the CD.
▶ Click on **Photocopiable Resources (PDF format)** to view a list of the photocopiables provided in the book that accompanies this CD.
▶ **Back**: click to return to the **opening screen**. Click **Continue** to move to the **Menu screen**.
▶ **Quit**: click **Quit** to close the menu program and progress to the **Quit screen.** If you quit from the **Quit screen** you will exit the CD. If you do not quit you will return to the **Menu screen**.

Resource Galleries

▶ **Help**: click **Help** to find support on accessing and using images.
▶ **Back to menu**: click here to return to the **Menu screen**.
▶ **Quit**: click here to move to the **Quit screen** – see **Quit** above.

Viewing images

Small versions of each image are shown in the Resource Gallery. Click and drag the slider on the slide bar to scroll through the images in the Resource Gallery, or click on the arrows to move the images frame by frame. Roll the pointer over an image to see the caption.

► Click on an image to view the screen-sized version of it.

► To return to the Resource Gallery click on **Back to Resource Gallery**.

Viewing videos

Click on the video icon of your choice in the Resource Gallery. In order to view the videos on this CD, you will need to have **QuickTime** installed on your computer (see 'Setting up your computer for optimal use' above).

Once at the video screen, use the buttons on the bottom of the video screen to operate the video. The slide bar can be used for a fast forward and rewind. To return to the Resource Gallery click on **Back to Resource Gallery**.

Listening to sound recordings

Click on the required sound icon. Use the buttons or the slide bar to hear the sound. A transcript will be displayed on the viewing screen where appropriate. To return to the Resource Gallery, click on **Back to Resource Gallery**.

Printing

Click on the image to view it (see 'Viewing images' above). There are two print options:

Print using Acrobat enables you to print a high-quality version of an image. Choosing this option means that the image will open as a read-only page in **Adobe Acrobat** and in order to access these files you will need to have already installed **Adobe Acrobat Reader** on your computer (see 'Setting up your computer for optimal use' above). To print the selected resource, select **File** and then **Print**. Once you have printed the resource **minimise** or **close** the Adobe screen using — or **X** in the top right-hand corner of the screen. Return to the Resource Gallery by clicking on **Back to Resource Gallery**.

Simple print enables you to print a lower quality version of the image without the need to use **Adobe Acrobat Reader**. Select the image and click on the **Simple print** option. After printing, click on **Back to Resource Gallery**.

Slideshow presentation

If you would like to present a number of resources without having to return to the Resource Gallery and select a new image each time, you can compile a slideshow. Click on the **+** tabs at the top of each image in the Resource Gallery you would like to include in your presentation (pictures, sound and video can be included). It is important that you click on the images in the order in which you would like to view them (a number will appear on each tab to confirm the order). If you would like to change the order, click on **Clear slideshow** and begin again. Once you have selected your images – up to a maximum of 20 – click on **Play slideshow** and you will be presented with the first of your selected resources. To move to the next selection in your slideshow click on **Next slide**, to see a previous resource click on **Previous slide**. You can end your slideshow presentation at any time by clicking on **Resource Gallery**. Your slideshow selection will remain selected until you **Clear slideshow** or return to the **Menu screen**.

Viewing on an interactive whiteboard or data projector

Resources can be viewed directly from the CD. To make viewing easier for a whole class, use a large monitor, data projector or interactive whiteboard. For group, paired or individual work, the resources can be viewed from the computer screen.

Photocopiable resources (PDF format)

To view or print a photocopiable resource page, click on the required title in the list and the page will open as a read-only page in **Adobe Acrobat**. In order to access these files you will need to have already installed **Adobe Acrobat Reader** on your computer (see 'Setting up your computer for optimal use' above). To print the selected resource select **File** and then **Print**. Once you have printed the resource **minimise** or **close** the Adobe screen using — or **X** in the top right-hand corner of the screen. This will take you back to the list of PDF files. To return to the **Menu screen**, click on **Back**.

MOVING AND GROWING

Content and skills

This chapter links to Unit 4A 'Moving and growing' of the QCA Scheme of Work for science at Key Stage 2. The Moving and Growing Resource Gallery on the CD-ROM, together with the teacher's notes and photocopiable pages in this chapter, can be used when teaching this unit of work.

Through this chapter, as with Unit 4A of the QCA Scheme of Work, children learn about the skeleton and its role in supporting the body. They learn about how the skeleton and muscles work to help them move. They also have the opportunity to compare human and animal skeletons. It may be useful to begin work on skeletons with the photocopiable page 'Outline of the human body' (page 17 and provided on the CD), as this is a good way of finding out what children already know about skeletons (see notes on pages 12–13).

The accompanying teacher's notes in the book include ways of using the resources with the whole class, for group work or with individual children. Some of the activities suggested will link with other areas of the curriculum such as English, maths, art or ICT. Wherever possible the activities encourage the children to ask questions and develop an enquiring approach to their learning.

Resources on the CD-ROM

The CD-ROM contains an illustration of a complete human skeleton and photographs of the skeletons of a pigeon, fish and snake, so that children can compare skeletons from different classes of the animal kingdom. There are X-ray photographs of parts of the human body, including an X-ray of a broken leg. There are also illustrations to show the musculature of the human body and photographs to show the movement of animals that do not have skeletons.

The CD-ROM has an interview with a Leicester Tigers first team rugby player, Tim Stimpson. This video shows Tim training and explains why he trains and exercises.

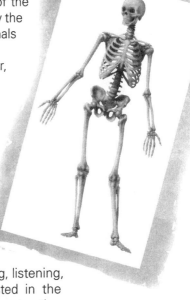

Photocopiable pages

The photocopiable pages in the book are also provided in PDF format on the CD-ROM and can be printed out from there. They include:
▶ word cards with the essential vocabulary for the topic
▶ an outline of the human body for children to draw a skeleton or muscles in
▶ an information sheet about Marie Curie
▶ a diary for children to record their exercise.

Science and literacy skills

Skills such as observing, questioning, describing, finding out, sorting, sequencing, listening, speaking, reading, writing and drawing are needed for the activities suggested in the teacher's notes. For example, feeling and describing the sequence of muscle contraction and relaxation in their arms will help children to learn how their bones and muscles work together to enable them to move, while helping them to practise their speaking and listening skills. Children are encouraged to find out about the use of X-rays, and to find out more about how creatures with external skeletons move and grow, developing their skills in researching and ICT use.

NOTES ON THE CD-ROM RESOURCES

SKELETONS

Human skeleton, Pigeon skeleton, Fish skeleton, Snake skeleton

Children do not need to know the scientific name for every bone in the body; but they should know, and be able to identify and locate, some of the major bones such as the skull, the spine and the ribs. Some children may enjoy finding out the correct names for the leg or arm bones. Children also need to realise that many other animals, beside humans, have bony skeletons inside them. From looking at the photographs of the pigeon, fish and snake skeletons, they will be able to compare skeletons and start to identify similarities and differences.

Discussing the pictures

▶ Look first at the illustration of the 'Human skeleton'. Ask the children to feel their own arms or legs. Can they feel the bones inside the muscles? Are all their bones as easy to feel?

▶ Talk about the role of the skeleton in supporting the body. Ask what the children think would happen to their bodies if they had no skeleton. How would they move?

▶ Focus on the enlarged ends of the bones in the illustration of the 'Human skeleton'. Explain how these act as anchor points for ligaments and muscles, and how this allows us to move our limbs so that we can walk upright.

▶ Discuss the characteristics of bone: how it is hard and strong, but can be broken if undue stress is put upon it.

▶ Ask the children to think about how big they were as babies and how big they are now. Are their bones the same size as when they were babies, or have they grown?

▶ Ask the children to find and name some of the bones in their body, such as the skull, ribs and spine.

▶ Look at the photographs of the 'Pigeon skeleton', 'Fish skeleton' and 'Snake skeleton'. Can the children find the spine in each one?

▶ Explain how very old bones can tell us a great deal about the animals they belonged to. Talk about how fossil dinosaur bones provide evidence that tells us about the creatures that lived millions of years ago.

Activities

▶ Give the children copies of the bone word cards on photocopiable pages 14 and 15 and ask them to look up any words they don't know, such as *tibia* or *humerus*.

▶ Let the children use the word cards on photocopiable pages 14 and 15 to label some of the bones in the pictures. They could find out the names of some other bones and add more labels to the pictures.

▶ Show the children the pictures and compare the different skeletons. Can they find the same bones in every picture? Are the bones the same or different? Why might they be different? For example, look at the adaptation of the forelimbs in the pigeon to form wings and in the fish to produce fins. Note the greater number of ribs in the snake.

▶ Ask the children to write a short piece about the function of the skeleton, thinking about its role in supporting the body and in allowing movement.

▶ Let the children use white paint to superimpose the skeleton on pictures of animals taken from magazines. They can use the skeleton photographs as a guide.

▶ Ask the children to make close observational drawings from boiled and bleached chicken or rabbit bones. Do not give untreated bones to the children. It may be possible to obtain a bone of a larger animal, sawn in half to show the internal structure, from a butcher, but this too must be properly treated and safe to handle.

▶ Make a collection of fossils and ask the children to research what the animals would have looked like.

X-RAYS OF THE HUMAN SKELETON

Skull X-ray, Hand X-ray, Broken leg X-ray

Children at this age should understand that although bones are strong, they can break. The development of X-rays has enabled doctors to 'see' exactly where and how a bone has been broken. The X-ray of the broken leg shows clearly how both the tibia and the fibula have been broken. Although it is a very useful tool, there are dangers in being exposed to X-rays too frequently, so they are used only when essential.

The X-ray of the skull also enables us to see how it grows. At birth, the bones of the skull are not fused together and there is a 'soft spot' in the centre called the fontanelle. This is to allow the baby to pass through the birth canal, and also to allow the skull to grow. As the baby grows, the bones become harder and gradually fuse together and the fontanelle disappears. The hard skull then provides a protective covering for the brain.

Discussing the photographs

▶ Look at the 'Hand X-ray' together and ask the children whether they can tell you what they are looking at. Can they identify the particular part of the body shown?

▶ Talk about the type of photograph that this is, and explain that X-rays allow us to see hard parts inside bodies.

▶ Look at the 'Skull X-ray' and point out the suture lines. Explain that this is where the plates of the skull join, and how this allows the skull to grow from baby to adult size.

▶ Ask the children whether any of them have ever had a broken bone. Did they have to have an X-ray taken? Can they tell the rest of the class what happened?

▶ Look at the 'Broken leg X-ray'. Ask whether the children can identify the part of the body being shown (the lower part of the leg between the knee and the ankle). Tell the children that these bones are called the tibia and the fibula.

▶ Talk about how bone can mend itself, but needs to be set properly so that the bone can still function as it did before. If a child has had a broken bone, he or she can perhaps describe how it was treated. Did he or she have a cast to support the broken bone? How long did it take to mend? Can he or she still tell where the bone was broken?

▶ Explain to the children that until fairly recently, when it was realised that too many X-rays could be dangerous, they were much more widely used. For example, X-rays were not only used in hospitals. Children going for a new pair of shoes would have their feet measured by X-ray to make sure they got the correct size and fit.

Activities

▶ Use the word cards on photocopiable pages 14 and 15 for the children to see how to spell some of the names of the bones such as *tibia* and *fibula*.

▶ Measure the forearm length and the head circumference of of children of different age ranges and adults in the school. How do the different ages compare? Does the oldest person have the longest forearm?

▶ In PE, ask the children to think about which bones are helping them to move as they go through different exercises.

▶ Ask the children to try to move as if they had no bones. Is it easier or more difficult? Could they stand upright?

▶ Ask the children to research the invention of X-rays. They can use the information on Marie Curie on photocopiable page 17, as well as books and other CD-ROMs.

MUSCLES

Front view of muscles, Back view of muscles

The two illustrations of the muscles in the human body will help children to learn that the muscles are attached to the skeleton, and that it is the tension between muscle and bone that enables us to move as we do. The muscles work in pairs, and as one muscle contracts the other relaxes. For example, as the muscle in the front of the thigh contracts the muscle at the back relaxes and the knee is bent. Muscles can only contract or relax.

Discussing the illustrations

▶ Look at the illustrations and point out how the muscles are in layers over the skeleton. Explain to the children how the muscles are attached to the bones with ligaments and how this helps us to move our limbs.

▶ Point out the white areas on both illustrations to the children and explain that these are areas where there is little or no muscle coverage.

▶ Talk about how some muscles are bigger than others. For example, the leg muscles are bigger than most since they have to move the weight of our bodies as we run and walk. Point these muscles out to the children on the illustrations.

▶ Talk about how muscles can only contract (shorten), an active process, or relax, a passive process; and how they usually work in pairs, with one muscle contracting as the opposing muscle relaxes.

▶ Discuss the fact that muscles increase in size and strength through exercise, but deteriorate quite rapidly if not used. Talk about the importance of regular exercise to keep our muscles working well.

▶ Tell the children that muscles control the smallest movement of our bodies, even the blink of an eye. Muscles even control movements inside us.

▶ Talk about how we use muscles in our faces to speak and to show emotions.

Activities

▶ Ask the children to feel their own muscles in their arms as they bend and straighten them. Show them how to feel the biceps muscle first, at the front of the upper arm, and to feel how it becomes rounder and harder as it shortens or contracts. Then ask them to notice how it becomes softer as the muscle relaxes when the arm straightens. Get the children to repeat the movement, but this time show them how to feel the triceps muscle at the back of the upper arm. This muscle tenses when the arm straightens.

▶ Give the children copies of the muscle word cards on photocopiable page 16 so they can see the words *biceps* and *triceps*.

▶ Ask the children to feel their own thigh or calf and then to feel their kneecap. Can they feel the difference between the thick muscle and the bony areas where there is little or no muscle?

▶ In PE, let the children work in pairs and take turns to watch each other move. Ask them to watch the legs of their partner and see whether they can tell which muscle is contracting or shortening, and which is relaxing. Ask them to explain how their muscles are helping them to move.

▶ Ask the children to write a short piece about how muscles work. Remind them to mention how they work in pairs, with one muscle relaxing as the other contracts. They could use the word cards on photocopiable page 16 to help them.

▶ Give each child a mirror and ask the children to show emotions on their faces. For example, they could look happy, angry, sad, and so on. Can a partner guess which emotion they are trying to show? What enables them to move their faces? Which muscles are being used? (For example, lip muscles or jaw muscles.)

▶ Show the children how to use found materials and elastic bands to make a model arm that moves at the elbow.

▶ Play the 'Interview: Being a sportsman' (provided on the CD). Make sure the children look in particular at the muscles working when Tim Stimpson is working out in the gym and when he is running.

Animals without skeletons, Snail, Beetle, Butterfly

Children should understand that not all animals have an internal skeleton to support their bodies. Some, such as insects and crustaceans, have a hard exoskeleton that supports their internal organs. Others, such as snails and slugs, are supported by fluid in their body cavities and cells. Two of the chief advantages of an exoskeleton are that it provides firm anchor points for muscles and protection for soft body parts.

Discussing the photographs

▶ Discuss the fact that not all animals have a skeleton to support them. Show each of the photographs to the children and ask whether they can suggest how the bodies of the animals are supported. Animals such as beetles and adult insects have a hard shell or exoskeleton. Other soft-bodied creatures, such as snails and worms, rely on fluid within their body cells and body cavities to give them support.

▶ Show the children the 'Snail' photograph and explain how its shell is for protection against predators and the weather, rather than for support. Tell them that as the snail grows it adds to its shell to make room for its larger body.

▶ Talk about how some creatures with external skeletons, such as crabs or beetles, need to moult or shed their skins in order to grow. The old skin splits and peels away, leaving a soft, new skin that gradually hardens to form the new shell. Such animals are particularly vulnerable to predators during this time.

▶ Look at the 'Butterfly' photograph. Discuss the fact that tiny muscles allow the butterfly to flap its wings so that it can fly. Tell the children that butterflies grow during the caterpillar stage and that the caterpillar moults and sheds its skin as it gets bigger. Butterflies often have a very short lifespan, their main goal being to mate before they die.

Activities

▶ Ask the children to compare one of the animals in the photographs with a human (they could use a classmate for comparison). Get them to make a list of similarities and differences between the two, and make sure that they mention skeletons.

▶ Collect some snails and look at them carefully as a class. Do they all have the same number of coils on their shells? Which snail do the children think is the oldest? Do all the shells spiral in the same direction?

▶ Make a collection of seashells. Look at the number of coils or ridges on the shells. Do the largest ones have more coils or ridges?

▶ Encourage the children to find out about other creatures that have no skeletons, such as worms, jellyfish or octopuses. What are they like? How are their bodies supported?

▶ Let the children look at a woodlouse with a hand lens. Look for the hard plates of its external skeleton, and ask the children to think about why these are separate plates. Help them by comparing it with a man wearing a suit of armour. Explain how the different plates allow some flexibility. Ask the children to write about how these plates allow the creature to move while protecting it.

▶ Watch a snail climb up the side of a plastic fish tank. Ask the children to comment on how it moves. ask: *What is helping it to move? Can you see the muscle in its foot rippling as it moves?*

▶ Let the children use the Internet or reference books to find out more about creatures with exoskeletons, such as how often they moult. Make a class information book from what the children find out to add to the class library.

Video: Being a sportsman

This video clip is an interview with a Leicester Tigers first team rugby player, Tim Stimpson. In it, Tim illustrates how a sportsman needs to keep his body healthy through exercise and training, and also the importance of eating the correct diet. It shows how body strength is improved by training in the gym, but also how Tim needs to train outside on the field to improve his speed, stamina and skills.

Discussing the interview

▶ Watch the video with the children. Draw their attention to how the shapes of Tim's muscles change as he lifts the heavy weights in the gym. Can the children see how the muscles contract and relax? Can they tell you why he exercises his muscles regularly in this way?

▶ Ask the children what they think would happen to our muscles if they had no exercise.

▶ Ask why the children think a sportsman sometimes needs to wear protective clothing. Compare the use of a headguard to an exoskeleton giving added protection to the brain.

▶ Discuss the importance of eating a suitable diet. Ask the children what sort of things Tim eats and what he avoids. Why does he avoid chips, crisps and fizzy drinks? Explain that sportsmen and women need to eat more food because they take a lot of exercise and use a lot of energy. People who take less exercise need to eat less, or they will put on too much weight.

▶ Ask the children whether they know anyone who trains hard for some kind of sport. What do they do? How do they train? Do they have a special diet?

Activities

▶ Take the children outside and encourage them to exercise and 'train' to improve their fitness and develop their sports skills.

▶ Ask the children to find out more about other sports that people train for. For example, do athletes such as runners and long jumpers all do the same kind of training?

▶ Ask the children to find out more about what different types of athletes eat.

▶ If possible, arrange a visit to a local football or rugby club for the children to watch a training session.

▶ Ask each child to keep a diary of the exercise they take during one week. They can use the 'Exercise diary' (photocopiable page 19). Remind the children to include PE lessons and playground games in their diary. At the end of the week, get the children to share their information and ask questions to find out things such as who walks to school or who goes swimming. Does anyone play football, rugby, go to judo or karate or belong to some other sports club?

▶ Discuss the exercise diaries kept during the week. Is this enough exercise? How could it be improved if not?

NOTES ON THE PHOTOCOPIABLE PAGES

Word cards PAGES 14–16

These word cards contain some of the basic vocabulary for the children to use and learn when learning about 'Moving and growing'. They include:
▶ words relating to bones
▶ words relating to muscles
Read through the words with the children. Ask which words they have heard before. Are there any words they don't understand?

Activities

▶ Spread the cards out on a table and ask the children to find specific words.

▶ Use the words as a word bank to help the children with their writing on this unit.

▶ Ask the children to use the word cards to label a large picture of a skeleton. They could find out the names of more bones and muscles and make additional labels to attach to the picture.

Outline of the human body PAGE 17

This outline of the human body can be used in several ways to assess the children's knowledge. They could be asked to draw their idea of a skeleton inside the outline before starting the unit, as an assessment of what they already know. At the end of the unit, it could be used to assess what the children have learned.

Discussing the illustration

▶ Look at the body outline and discuss with the children what they would expect to find inside their own bodies. Make sure they mention the skeleton, muscles and major internal organs, such as the heart, liver and lungs.

▶ Ask them to feel their own arms and legs and describe what they feel.

▶ Introduce or revisit the function of the skeleton. Talk about how it supports the body and protects the internal organs.

▶ Name some of the larger bones and discuss where they are in the body.

Activities

▶ Create a slide show combining the picture of the 'Human skeleton' with the 'Outline of the human body', so that the children can see the relationship between the skeleton and the body shape. Then give each child a copy of the body outline and ask them to draw the human skeleton inside it. How accurate are their drawings?

▶ At the end of the unit, give each child a fresh copy of the body outline picture and ask them to draw the human skeleton inside it again. Use this to assess their learning.

Marie Curie

PAGE 18

X-rays are in common use today and are still the most effective means of pinpointing fractures in bones. Marie Curie and her husband, Pierre, were instrumental in discovering the radioactive elements that make X-rays possible. Unfortunately, no-one at that time realised the dangers of the materials they were working with, and both Marie and Pierre suffered from radiation sickness.

Discussing the text

▶ Ask the children whether any of them have ever had an X-ray for any reason. Can they tell the class about it?

▶ Ask whether any of the children have heard of Marie Curie and her discoveries.

▶ Give the children time to read the information sheet on page 18 and talk about what the Curies discovered.

▶ Ask the children whether they can tell you, from the information on the sheet, why it can be dangerous for a person to have too many X-rays.

Activities

▶ Ask the children to answer the questions on the sheet by finding out more information.

▶ Tell the children to make a note of anything else of interest that they find out while they are doing their research.

▶ Let the children work in small groups and prepare a presentation of their findings, then give it to the rest of the class.

▶ Find out why polonium is so called (Marie Curie named it after her native Poland).

▶ Why has radium been replaced as the luminous material used to make the hands of a clock visible in the dark?

Exercise diary

PAGE 19

This is a simple grid for the children to complete throughout the week, logging all the exercise they take. Make sure that the children understand what they are expected to do, and remind them to take the diaries home and bring them back each day. It might be an idea to make a list of the children's estimated hours beforehand, so that the completed diaries can be matched realistically against the estimates!

After the diary has been completed, interrogate the data to find out which is the most common type of exercise and which is the least common. What else does the data reveal?

Bone word cards (1)

bones

spine

femur

tibia

fibula

Bone word cards (2)

humerus

ribs

skull

jaw

skeleton

exoskeleton

Muscle word cards

muscles
biceps
triceps
contract
relax
tension

Outline of the human body

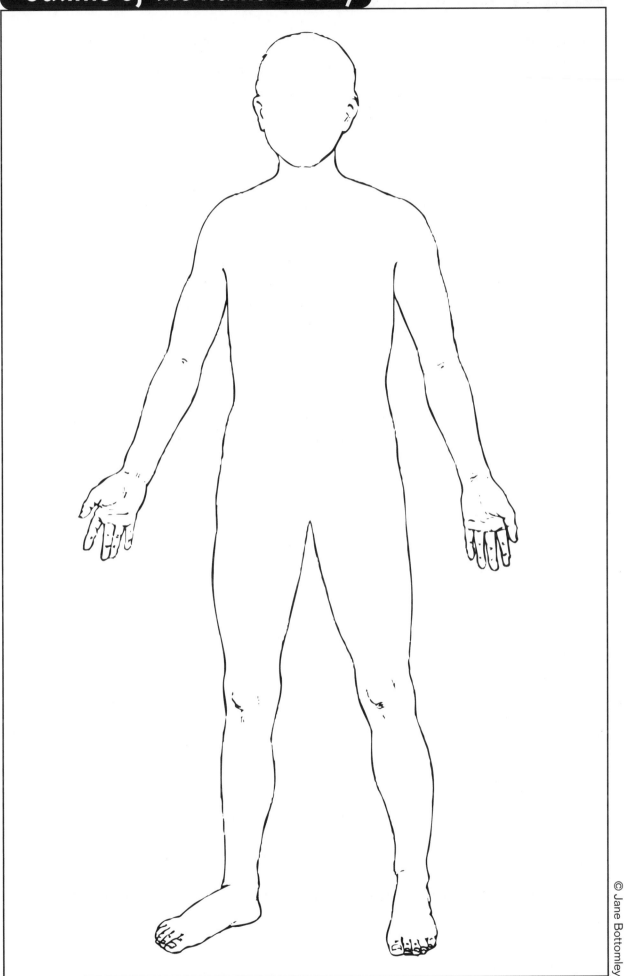

© Jane Bottomley

Marie Curie (1867–1934)

Marie Curie was born in Poland in 1867. She studied physics at the Sorbonne in Paris. She married her husband, Pierre Curie, in 1895 and they subsequently worked together. They discovered polonium and radium, for which they received the Nobel Prize for physics in 1903.

Pierre earned a living by teaching, but together they worked on the mineral pitchblende to find out why it was so radioactive even after uranium had been extracted from it. Their laboratory was little more than a rough shed, and at that time the dangers of radioactivity were unknown. They took no precautions to safeguard their health. Pierre even carried a small piece of radium around in his pocket to show his friends. Marie liked to keep a small sample at the side of her bed, because it shone in the dark.

Marie died in 1934 of leukaemia, caused by prolonged exposure to radioactive materials. Her notebooks are too contaminated to handle even today.

Pierre died after an accident in 1906, but Marie continued the work and was awarded a second Nobel Prize in 1911, this time for chemistry. She was the first scientist to win the Nobel Prize twice.

She studied the application of radioactivity to medicine, and pioneered mobile X-ray units as head of the French Radiological Service during the First World War.

Find out more:
1. What other scientists have shared the Nobel prize? in 1903?
2. What did these scientists discover?
3. Why did the Curies not apply for a patent for their discoveries?
4. How did Pierre die?

Record any other interesting things you find out about Marie and Pierre Curie.

Exercise diary

Keep a diary for a week of ALL the exercise you do during each day. Before you begin, estimate how many hours you will spend exercising during the week. _____ hours

Day	At school	Total time spent	After school	Total time spent
Monday				
Tuesday				
Wednesday				
Thursday				
Friday				
Saturday				
Sunday				
	Total		Total	

How many hours did you spend exercising? _____ hours

What sort of exercise do you take on a regular basis? _____

_____

Do you think you need to take more exercise? _____

HABITATS

Content and skills

This chapter links to Unit 4B 'Habitats' of the QCA Scheme of Work for science at Key Stage 2. The Habitats Resource Gallery on the CD-ROM, together with the teacher's notes and photocopiable pages in this chapter, can be used in the teaching of this unit.

Through this chapter, as with Unit 4B of the QCA Scheme of Work, the children are helped to understand the concept of habitats and extend their knowledge of animals and plants in their local environment. They learn about how animals depend on other organisms (either plant or animal) for their food, and how they can only live, grow and thrive in a suitable habitat that offers such things as shelter and a reliable food source. Pictures of paired organisms help children to identify similarities and differences between plants and animals in order to build on their understanding of classification. Work in this chapter also helps children to learn about food chains, the interdependence of all living things and how disruption of a food chain can be disastrous for other organisms in that chain.

The accompanying teacher's notes in the book include ways of using the resources with the whole class, for group work or with individual children. Some of the activities suggested will link with other areas of the curriculum such as maths, art, English or history. Wherever possible the activities encourage the children to ask questions and develop an enquiring approach to their learning.

Resources on the CD-ROM

The CD-ROM contains labelled diagrams of simple food chains that will lead children to devise their own chains. Photographs of a range of plants and animals, including example of vertebrates and invertebrates and of herbivores and carnivores, form the basis of work on the variety of life and the interdependence of species. Pictures of a variety of organisms and a photocopiable key are provided to help the children develop classification skills. Photographs of 'unfamiliar locals' are included, as well as images of various animals eating (including a lion eating its prey).

Photocopiable pages

The photocopiable pages in the book are also provided in PDF format on the CD-ROM and can be printed out from there. They include:
▶ word cards with the essential vocabulary for the topic
▶ an information sheet about making and using a flower press
▶ simple keys for classification
▶ poems about insects.

Science and literacy skills

Skills such as observing, questioning, finding out, describing, sorting, sequencing, listening, speaking, reading, writing and drawing are needed for the activities suggested in the teacher's notes. For example, the children will discuss and devise a variety of food chains and make mathematical nets in order to represent the food chains three-dimensionally, They will also sort organisms according to their own and given criteria and their observable features. In discussion, they will learn and use appropriate vocabulary such as 'predator' and 'prey'.

NOTES ON THE CD-ROM RESOURCES

ORGANISMS

Plants: Horse chestnut tree, Grass, Daisies, Dandelions, Wheat

Vertebrates: Human, Seal, Salmon, Eagle, Tortoise, Snake

Invertebrates: Snail, Slug, Worm, Fly, Starfish, Crab

Children often think that invertebrates and human beings are not animals, and that trees are not plants. Most living things that children come across in their lives are either plant or animal (fungi are now put in a separate category). Children need to begin to understand the vast diversity of living things, and the idea that each organism is suited to the environment in which it lives.

Discussing the photographs

▶ Look at each photograph in turn with the children. Ask them to identify the organism in each.

▶ Can they say whether each photograph is of an animal or a plant? Talk about the fact that all of the photographs show living things and that all living things are organisms. Explain that almost all living things, except for fungi, are either animals or plants – including humans and trees.

▶ Ask the children to name some more organisms from both the animal and plant kingdoms. List these on the board.

▶ Tell the children that the list only contains a tiny fragment of the organisms that inhabit the Earth and that there is a vast variety of plants and animals, some of which have not yet been discovered.

▶ Look at all the photographs and talk about the fact that creatures such as the human, seal and salmon have a backbone and are vertebrates, and those such as the slug and worm have no backbone and are called invertebrates. Can the children identify the other vertebrates and invertebrates in the photographs?

▶ Ask them whether they know what the word *habitat* means. Can they tell you why habitats vary and the species that live in them are different? Ask whether they think a desert cactus lives in the same habitat as a rain forest tree. Why not? (A cactus is adapted to store water, and can therefore live in a very dry habitat.)

▶ Ask the children what the words *herbivore* (plant eater), *carnivore* (meat eater) and *omnivore* (meat and plant eater) mean. Can they name some animals that fall into each category? Which do humans belong to?

▶ Tell the children that some plants, such as sundews and Venus fly traps, live in habitats where the soil cannot supply all of their nutritional needs, and that they are adapted to consume insects. The insect nutrients are supplementary to the food the plant produces using sunlight.

Activities

▶ Ask the children to sort and group the photographs according to their own criteria and to explain their reasons for sorting the organisms in a particular way.

▶ Ask the children to sort the photographs into sets according to given criteria, such as: plant or animal; vertebrate or invertebrate; herbivore, omnivore or carnivore. Let the children use secondary sources to find out which category to place an organism in if necessary.

▶ Challenge the children to think of another animal or plant for each set they have sorted the photographs into.

▶ Laminate copies of the photographs to play Matching Pairs. Place all the cards face down on a table and encourage each child to turn up two cards at a time. If they can give a valid reason for putting the two organisms together (for example, the eagle and the seal are carnivores, or the slug and the worm are invertebrates), they can keep the pair. If not, the cards are turned face down again for the next child's turn. The child with the most pairs at the end of the game is the winner. Challenge the children to make groups of three and say why these match. You could add some cards with extra animals from the CD if you wish.

▶ Give the children some of the photographs and ask them to classify these. An example of how to use a key is provided on 'Making a key' (photocopiable page 34).

PAIRS

Bee, Wasp, Spider, Beetle, Daisies, Dandelions

In order to classify organisms into more specific types, it is necessary to look at the individual features of each one. Children at this age need, therefore, to begin to look in more detail at the observable features of individual organisms. At this stage it is enough for them to begin to identify the similarities and differences between groups of organisms. However, children often have more difficulty with identifying similarities than with identifying differences, and may need some help.

It is helpful to think of the photographs in this group as pairs: bee/wasp, spider/beetle, daisies/dandelions. Pairing them will help the children to identify the similarities and differences between the organisms. For example, the bee and the wasp are winged, have six legs, are stripy and have stings. But the stripes on the wasp are more distinct than those on the bee. The beetle and the spider have fewer similarities – the beetle is an insect and the spider is an arachnid; they have six and eight legs respectively. The spider has no wings and the beetle has no observable wings (unless it is flying). Daisies and dandelions are both complex flowers consisting of lots of tiny florets. They both have one head on the end of each stem and the flowers are carried on stems above a rosette of leaves.

Discussing the photographs

▶ Look at all the photographs with the children. Discuss the similarities and differences between the organisms shown. For example, talk about the number of legs, wings and eyes, the different colours and so on. List these on the board and add any important points that the children have missed.

▶ Put the photographs together in the following pairs: bee/wasp, spider/beetle, daisies/dandelions. Look at them again. Can the children tell you why the organisms could be paired in this way? Ask them to identify as many similarities as they can in each pairing.

▶ Look at the pairs again and ask the children to identify as many differences as they can. Do the similarities outnumber the differences?

▶ Are the children able to tell you about other possible ways of grouping the animals? For example, the bee/wasp and spider/beetle pairs could be grouped together as these organisms are all animals. They could not be grouped as insects, however, because the spider is an arachnid.

Activities

▶ Give the children copies of the photographs and challenge them to find as many different ways of grouping the organisms into sets as they can, explaining the groupings.

▶ Let the children practise using collecting equipment, such as pooters, soft brushes and collecting jars, in the classroom before going outside and collecting as wide a range of minibeasts and plants as possible in a way that won't harm them. Torn and rolled-up tissue can be used in the classroom to represent creatures for the children to practise with. Explain that the children should take care when collecting plant samples and only pick, for example, one leaf and one flower, and only from common species. Once back in the classroom, help the children to group the minibeasts and plants according to observable features. Make sure that any living creatures are handled with care and sensitivity and are returned to their habitat as soon as possible.

▶ Ask the children to choose one of the organisms in the photographs and to make a close observational drawing of it.

▶ Let the children press specimens of plants and flowers so that they can keep a record of what different plants and flowers look like, finding their similarities and differences. Give the children a copy of 'Making a flower press' (photocopiable page 35) for them to follow and let them make a simple flower press.

▶ The children could make enlarged models of some of the creatures they have studied, using reclaimed materials. Encourage them to make sure that as many of the defining features of the animals as possible are represented accurately, for example the number of legs, wings and eyes.

▶ Ask small groups of children to devise a leaflet about a particular pair of organisms, drawing the observable features, describing why the organisms have been paired and noting similarities and differences between the organisms. The leaflets can then be displayed alongside copies of the photographs of the pairs of organisms from the CD.

▶ Read the poems 'My Praying Mantis' by John Lyons (photocopiable page 33) and 'The Spider' by Frank Collymore (photocopiable page 34) with the children, for fun and to reinforce their knowledge of the wide variety of living things.

HABITATS

Natural pond, Grassy field, Woodland, Plant trough, Hedge

Children need to be introduced to the word *habitat* and to realise that there are many different types of habitat, both locally and further afield, that vary in size and diversity. When comparing habitats it is helpful for children to choose habitats of a similar scale, for example fields, woodland and ponds, or mini-habitats such as a tree, a section of hedge, a flower bed and a small grassy area. They could also compare micro-habitats, such as under a leaf, a log and a stone.

It is always best to go out and look at habitats, but the photographs could be used to remind the children of similar locations or to illustrate types of habitat that they have not been able to visit. Children who are not able to visit a variety of habitats could use secondary sources to find out what kinds of organisms they would expect to find in each habitat.

In a pond, children could expect to see frogs, newts, toads, water plants, beetles and small water creatures such as water fleas. A pond also provides places for some partly aquatic animals, such as dragonflies, to lay their eggs. Ponds are also an important source of water for small mammals and birds.

A grassy field provides a habitat for plants that benefit from open areas in full sun. The types of plants found will depend on the soil type and whether the field is grazed, mown or unmanaged. Fields are home to many insects and small mammals that feed on the plants. Some birds like to nest at ground level too.

In a wooded area trees provide shade and shelter. Conifers or evergreens provide a constant dense canopy, so little grows under them. Deciduous woods may have bluebells and other plants that grow in spring before the canopy becomes too dense for them to get the sunlight they require. Woodlands are home to a wide variety of birds and other creatures that find shelter and a rich food source in the trees.

A plant trough is essentially a made habitat, but is still attractive to insects. Sometimes mosses will establish themselves there. The choice of plants in the trough may dictate the type of creature attracted to it. This is a habitat that the children could make. Filled with herbs or plants, such as lavender or nasturtiums, they will attract a variety of insects.

Hedges provide a rich source of food and good shelter for many different insects, birds and small mammals. They also often act as 'wildlife corridors', enabling creatures to move from area to area. The more different species of plants there are in a hedge, the older it tends to be.

Discussing the photographs

▶ Talk with the children about the definition of a habitat. (A habitat provides the organisms found there with the conditions for life.)

▶ Look at each of the photographs and ask the children to identify each habitat.

▶ Discuss the fact that organisms need particular conditions in which to live, grow and thrive. Ask the children to tell you some of the plants and animals they think might be found in each of the habitats in the photographs. Are there any organisms that might be found in several or most of the habitats? (For example, grass or ants.)

▶ Explain that an organism such as grass is less specialised than some other organisms and is found in a wider range of habitats than, for example, wild orchids.

Activities

▶ Ask the children to look again at the photographs of a selection of animals and plants from the Organisms and Pairs sections of this unit. Ask them to choose one or two of these and to match each one to the photograph of the particular habitat that it would fit into. Can they say why they have matched the organism to that habitat?

▶ Take the children out and look at some habitats in the locality. Ask the children to note how they are different and how they are the same. Look for the different plants and animals in each habitat.

▶ Let the children work together in pairs to make lists of the plants and animals they found in one of the habitats in the photographs.

▶ Ask the children to compare two of the habitats. Are some of the species found in both habitats the same? Are some different?

▶ Ask the children to choose a particular animal or plant and to write about what conditions it needs in order to live, and why it is found in a particular habitat. The conditions might relate to food, shelter and so on. Encourage the children to use secondary sources, such as reference books, CD-ROMs or the Internet, to find out more if necessary.

UNFAMILIAR LOCALS

Shield bug, Bracket fungus, Newt, Teasel

Some organisms are less common in the environment, or are very good at hiding away. Shield bugs are very well camouflaged in shape and colour and are therefore difficult to spot, but are well worth the search. Bracket fungus is usually only found on dead or decaying trees, but is quite spectacular. Newts are fairly secretive creatures, and have declined in number due to ponds being drained or filled in with a consequent loss of habitat. Great crested newts are a protected species. Teasels may be unfamiliar to some children, though they are becoming more common in some areas. For example, they tend to spread along the verges of motorways. They provide a rich source of seeds for such seed-eating birds as finches.

The dependence of organisms on their habitats means that small environmental changes can often have a dramatic effect on some of the organisms living there. Children need to recognise the importance of protecting both the environment and the organisms found there in order to protect the diversity of living things. They should also be encouraged to think about the effects that specific changes, such as draining ponds, cutting down hedges or building motorways, could have on organisms.

Discussing the photographs

▶ Look at each of the photographs in turn. Can the children identify each of the organisms? Do they belong to the plant or animal kingdom? What about the fungus? (Fungi are categorised as a kingdom of their own.)

▶ Ask the children whether they have seen any of these organisms in the environment. Explain that some of them are not easy to find as they are good at hiding, like the newt and the shield bug, or are not common.

▶ Ask the children whether they know why some creatures are less common than others and why the numbers of some species are declining. Perhaps their habitat is less common or is being built on or farmed by humans, and so on. Frogs and toads are declining because of the decrease in the number of farm ponds. Where they can, they migrate to garden ponds. Skylarks and other ground nesting birds, such as corncrakes, are less common now because changes in farming methods have disrupted nesting sites.

▶ Talk about how some creatures are not always found in the environment because they are seasonal – for example, tadpoles are found only in the spring and early summer, and some birds may just be winter visitors.

Activities

▶ Let the children use reference books or the Internet to identify and find out more about the organisms in the photographs. Ask them to write two or three things about each organism. For example: what its habitat is like, whether it is an animal or a plant, what it eats (if it is an animal).

▶ Ask the children to use the Internet or other secondary sources to find out more about fungi. Ask them to decide whether fungi are animals or plants or neither.

▶ Take the children out and let them look for the organisms in the photographs. Make sure they make a note of where they found them and the type of habitat they were found in.

▶ Create a wildlife area in the school grounds, including a pond if possible, or encourage the children to take an active part in maintaining the present one.

▶ Let the class plant a tree in the school grounds. A crab apple tree provides blossom for bees and hoverflies and fruit eaten by blackbirds and thrushes.

▶ Set up nest boxes or bird tables for the children to investigate what foods are needed to attract different species.

▶ Organise a class debate between, for example, those who want to build a road or put up buildings that will affect a habitat where less common species thrive, and those who want to preserve the habitat of those species.

▶ Ask the children to write a leaflet explaining to others why it is important to care for the environment. For example, preserving species, aesthetic considerations and so on.

FOOD CHAINS

Vertical food chain, Horizontal food chains

It will be helpful to talk about the words *producer* and *consumer* when discussing food chains with the children, as these hold everyday meanings that the children may be familiar with: the producer is producing food for the consumer to eat. The words *predator* and *prey* are also relevant when discussing food chains and need to be explained to the children. Children often think that the arrow in a food chain means 'eats'. It could be helpful to tell children that the arrow means 'gives food to' in order to explain the direction in which it is pointing. Tell the children that food chains start with a green plant because plants produce their own food using the sunlight and don't consume other organisms (except in the case of carnivorous plants that supplement their food production by consuming insects). Children do not need to know the details of photosynthesis at this stage.

Children may come across food chains represented in different ways, and need to be able to understand them however they are shown. The 'Horizontal food chains' pictures show three different food chains represented horizontally for the children to compare. The 'Vertical food chain' picture gives an impression of the 'pyramid of numbers' in a food chain: the higher up the chain you look, the smaller the number of individuals.

Discussing the food chains

▶ Explain to the children that all living things form part of a food chain. Look at the 'Vertical food chain'. Point out how the things at the bottom are green plants (virtually all food chains start with a green plant) and the thing at the top is a large bird (predators such as lions, humans and large birds of prey are often at the top of a food chain).

▶ Talk about the fact that the species in the food chain are interdependent. Using the 'Vertical food chain', explain that if there were no green leaves for caterpillars to eat there would be no caterpillars, and then there would be no food for the robins that prey on the caterpillars. If there were no robins there would be no food for the hawk, and so there would be no hawk.

▶ Introduce the words *producer* and *consumer* and relate these to the organisms in a food chain to help the children understand how food chains work.

▶ Discuss some of the numerical ratios within a food chain. For example, in the 'Vertical food chain' it takes many leaves to sustain a caterpillar; many, but fewer, caterpillars to feed robins; and fewer still robins to feed a bird of prey.

▶ Using the 'Horizontal food chains', ask the children whether they can name the species in each food chain, starting with the green plants and working their way along the chain.

▶ Show the children the 'Horizontal food chains' and ask them what they think would happen if part of a food chain were to disappear. For example, if there were no frogs, no grass, or no caterpillars.

▶ Ask the children whether they can tell you what the words *predator* and *prey* mean. Do they think an organism is always a predator or a prey? Can a small bird be both?

Activities

▶ Use copies of either food chain with the pictures cut up for the children to reorder.

▶ As a class, make up as many different food chains as possible with a predator other than a human at the top of them. Can the children devise food chains with three or four species in them? (For example: a green plant, greenfly and ladybird; a caterpillar, blue tit and hawk.) What is the longest food chain the children can think of?

▶ Devise some class food chains with humans at the top. Can the children think of food chains with only two species in them? For example, wheat and a human.

▶ Challenge the children to devise some food chains for vegetarians.

▶ Represent all the food chains that the children have thought of either pictorially or with words, including arrows.

▶ Working with groups of four, ask the children to draw up a food chain consisting of four organisms. Then show the children how to draw a net for a cube. Ask each child in the group to draw some nets and to draw one of the organisms on one face of each net. Each child needs to make the same number of cubes as the number of that organism being shown in the chain. The cubes can then be used to construct a 'food chain pyramid'. For example, there could be eight cubes with leaves, four with caterpillars, two with blue tits and one with a hawk. Let the children build their pyramid with the leaves at the bottom and the hawk at the top. Then remove one of the cubes of one of the species near the bottom of the food chain to show how the rest of the chain collapses, thus demonstrating the dependence of the organism at the top of the chain on those at the bottom.

WHAT DO THEY EAT?

Thrush, Urban fox, Blue tit, Butterfly, Slug

Animals will only flourish if there is enough of the food they need available. Some species require a fairly specific diet – for example, the butterfly feeds solely on nectar. The thrush thrives on small invertebrates such as slugs and snails; while the blue tit eats small grubs, seeds and nuts, often relying for much of its food on garden feeders that help it to sustain its numbers. Slugs are vegetarian, eating a wide range of plant material.

Many species have adapted to living in habitats that are not entirely natural to them. For example, the urban fox lives in cities or towns and feeds on a diet of refuse, because its natural habitat has declined. Humans, sometimes unwittingly, supply the urban fox with food. Some foxes have found that there is a ready supply of food in dustbins and around houses and shops, so they have moved into the city from the countryside. Because of this plentiful supply of food, many foxes are now raising families in cities and their cubs are truly urbanised, never having lived in the countryside.

Discussing the photographs

▶ Look at each of the photographs in turn and ask the children to identify the creature, and to say what it is eating if possible.

▶ Ask the children to classify the creatures as herbivores, carnivores or omnivores.

▶ Ask the children to tell you whether the creatures are predators or prey. Are they sometimes both predators and prey?

▶ Talk about what sort of habitat each creature needs. Is the urban fox in the photograph in its natural habitat? When a creature adapts by changing where and how it lives, does it have a new habitat?

▶ Talk about the fact that creatures can only live where there is appropriate shelter and their food source is reliable. For example, thrushes are declining because there are now fewer suitable habitats and because of garden poisons, such as slug pellets, getting into their food chain and killing them. Talk also about how birds may rely on garden feeders and foxes on dustbins.

▶ Tell the children that when a creature's habitat begins to disappear, for any reason, the animals begin to fall in numbers and may die out unless they can adapt.

▶ Can the children tell you why some foxes have become urbanised?

Activities

▶ Help the children to make a habitat for slugs or snails and to devise and carry out a fair test to find out which food they like best. Slugs or snails may be kept in a plastic tank for a short time. Line the bottom with damp compost and cover the tank with a secure lid with air holes (snails really are the Houdinis of the animal world). Keep the tank somewhere cool out of direct sunlight and provide some large stones or an upturned margarine pot for shelter. Only keep the creatures for a short time; make sure that they are handled with care and sensitivity and returned to their habitat as soon as possible. Make sure the children always wash their hands after handling living things.

▶ The children could use reference books or the Internet to find out more about the habitat of each creature in the photographs.

▶ Ask the children to find out more about what each creature in the photographs eats. They could also find out what eats them.

▶ Ask the children to put each organism shown in the photographs into its own food chain. They could record the chains pictorially or in writing.

▶ Allow the children to choose one of the creatures in the photographs and write and illustrate an information sheet on it to make a class reference book.

Predator and prey

This photograph shows a lion eating a zebra. The lion is at the top of this particular food chain, which begins with grass, then goes to a zebra and finally a lion. Sometimes children associate the word *predator* with large carnivores, such as lions, and don't realise that creatures as small as spiders are also predators, eating small prey such as flies.

Discussing the photograph

▶ Look at the photograph with the children. Talk about the fact that the lion has killed the zebra for food and that the lion is at the top of this food chain. Explain that it is one of the largest predatory carnivores.

▶ Can the children tell whether the lion is male or female? How do they know? Look at the two lions in the background and ask the children whether they are male or female.

▶ Explain to the children how lions often hunt together in family groups called prides, and that it is usually the lionesses that do most of the hunting. Tell the children how the lion often eats first and what is left is eaten by the lionesses and their cubs.

▶ Tell the children that lions do not need to hunt every day: it depends on the size of their previous kill and how recent that was.

Activities

▶ Ask the children to find out where lions live and what animals they prey on.

▶ In groups, ask the children to find out about other predators, for example birds, fish, insects and spiders. What do they eat and how do they catch their prey? Do they hunt alone or in groups? Ask the groups to use the information they have found to prepare a presentation to the rest of the class.

▶ Take the children outside to look for spiders' webs and any prey caught in them.

NOTES ON THE PHOTOCOPIABLE PAGES

Word cards
PAGES 29–31

These word cards contain some of the basic vocabulary for the children to use and learn when learning about 'Habitats'. They include:
▶ words relating to life processes
▶ words relating to habitats and feeding.
Read through the words with the children. Ask which words the children have heard before. Are there any words they don't understand?

Activities

▶ Spread the word cards on a table and ask the children to find specific words.

▶ Ask the children to make a dictionary of words for this unit, using the word cards, and to add a definition to each one.

▶ Read out the definitions of some of the words and ask the children to supply the relevant word card for each one.

My Praying Mantis
PAGE 32

This poem by John Lyons is a good description of an insect predator that is then itself eaten by a mammalian predator – the cat!

Discussing the poem

▶ Read the poem through with the children. Talk about having a mantis as a pet. Would it be a good pet to have? Why?
▶ Ask the children what the mantis eats. Ask: *Is it a carnivore, herbivore or an omnivore? Is it really dangerous?*
▶ Discuss why people in the poem were curious when they saw the mantis.
▶ Ask the children about what happened to the mantis in the end. Was the mantis prey or predator?

Activities

▶ Ask the children to write a poem about another creature that is both predator and prey, for example a seal (seals are fish eaters but are eaten themselves by sharks or killer whales).
▶ Get the children to find out more about mantises. Where do they come from? What type of creature are they? The children can make an illustrated information booklet to share with the class.

The Spider   PAGE 33

This short poem by Frank Collymore encapsulates the 'essence' of a spider, and would be a good starting point for a discussion about conveying meaning or imagery in very few words.

Discussing the poem

▶ Ask the children to tell you what kind of creature the spider is. Discuss the fact that although a spider is often mistaken for an insect, it is really an arachnid.
▶ How can the children tell from the poem that the spider is a predator?
▶ Talk about the fact that the spider is a very efficient predator, but that it is sometimes preyed on by other species such as birds.
▶ Ask the children why they think the writer admires the spider and what it can do.

Activities

▶ Ask the class to find out whether all spiders make the same kind of web.
▶ Explain that not all spiders make webs. Ask the children to think about other ways that spiders catch their prey (jumping, stalking, ambushing, biting, and so on).
▶ Ask the children to choose a different creature and to say as much about it as they can in a poem of not more than eight lines.

Making a key   PAGE 34

Keys are used to classify different organisms through observing features and identifying similarities and differences. Children at this age will need to be able to use simple keys to help them identify plants and animals. This information page will explain to the children how to make a simple key.

Discussing the key

▶ Talk about how it is often useful or even necessary to identify a particular plant or animal. Explain how keys enable us to do this by recording observable features and identifying similarities and differences, which allows us to distinguish between organisms.
▶ Discuss with the children the formulation of questions that can only have *Yes* or *No* as an answer.

Activities

▶ Give the children copies of the 'Horse chestnut tree', 'Daisies', 'Salmon', 'Eagle' and 'Crab' photographs from the Habitats Resource Gallery so that they can follow the example on the sheet.
▶ Use 'Making a key' (photocopiable page 34) to support the children in making their own identification keys. The children will need several copies each of the sheet.
▶ Give the children a wider selection of plants and animals from the Habitats Resource Gallery so that they can construct a larger key. Display the key along with copies of the pictures.

Flower press

PAGE 35

Pressing flowers is a fun activity and is a useful way of making a record of plant species found. It has been used by botanists and collectors for a long time. Flowers pressed in this way retain their shape and some of their colour; though delicate, they are remarkably durable if handled with care. As well as being used as a scientific record, pressed flowers can be used for decoration in art and craft.

Discussing the sheet

▶ Talk to the children about how pressed flowers can be a useful record of plant species collected.

▶ Mention how collectors of new plant species in foreign countries pressed flowers as a record to bring home, since the voyages they went on often took too long for fresh flowers to survive. Sometimes they brought back seeds and growing plants in pots as well.

▶ Talk about the uses of pressed flowers in art and craft: boxes, lampshades, bookmarks, greetings cards and so on.

Activities

▶ The children can make flower presses, using the instructions on photocopiable page 35. Make sure that they have practised using a drill, and supervise their work closely.

▶ Go for a walk and collect some local flowers, or use bought flowers. Avoid fleshy or thick flowers, as these take a long time to press and dry. Flat-shaped flowers such as pansies work really well.

▶ Let the children press the flowers, leave them for several weeks and then mount the pressed flowers in a book (using sticky-backed plastic) to make a class record.

▶ The children can annotate the book pages with notes on which plants the flowers came from and where and when they were found. The book can be added to by other classes to build up a record of the flora in the local area.

▶ The children can use any spare flowers to make bookmarks, greetings cards and so on. They can mount the flowers on card cut to appropriate shapes, and cover them with sticky-backed plastic.

Life processes word cards

nutrition

feeding

reproduction

growth

birth

death

📖 SCHOLASTIC
PHOTOCOPIABLE

Habitats and feeding word cards (1)

habitat

condition

organism

food chain

key

Habitats and feeding word cards (2)

predator

prey

producer

consumer

My Praying Mantis

I once had a mantis as a pet.
A praying mantis; you must not forget,

is the tiger of the insect world,
hungry, fierce and extremely bold;

and if you are an insect, keep away
should a mantis be lurking where you play.

Anyway, my mantis was my very best friend.
He sat on my shoulder, and I did defend

his insect's right to stay with me,
protect him from people's curiosity;

for they thought it very strange
the way his body was arranged:

For a start, his neck was very long,
and his heart-shaped head did not belong

to that thin neck and bulbous abdomen
or toothed arms as strong as ten,

wings which gave him speed in flight
when he attacked and with delight

grabbed a cockroach for his supper,
tore and ate it with his choppers.

However, one day, Phoebe, the neighbour's cat,
gobbled up my mantis and that was that.

Phoebe licked her lips, seemed satisfied
with a chewed-up mantis in her inside.

I suppose, for a mantis, the moral to this story
is, look out for cats or you'll be sorry.

John Lyons

The Spider

I'm told that the spider
Has coiled up inside her
Enough silky material
To spin an aerial
One-way track
to the moon and back;
Whilst I
Cannot even catch a fly.

Frank Collymore

Making a key

Look at the pictures and think of a question that will divide them into two groups. For example, *Is it a plant?*

The question must only have the answer *Yes* or *No.*

Write the question in the first box.

Write the names of the pictures in the box under the appropriate answer.

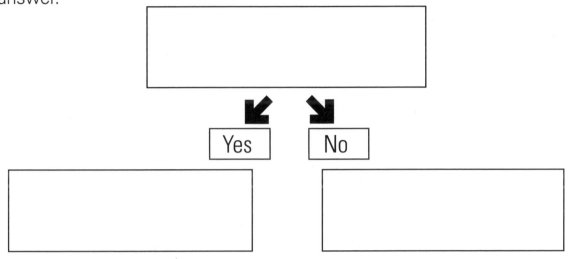

Choose one of the groups above and write another question to divide the pictures in it. The question must only have the answer *Yes* or *No* again.

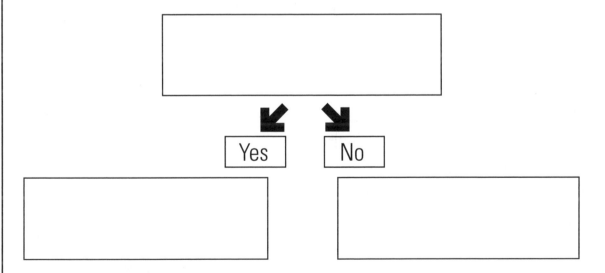

Continue asking more questions until only one picture remains. Use a reference book to identify the organism, and write its name in the box.

Now do the same with the other main group of pictures.

Collect all the pictures together and ask a friend whether they can use your key to identify each picture.

Making a flower press

You will need:

2 pieces of wood or MDF (1cm thick, approximately 25cm × 25cm).
4 long bolts with fly nuts and 8 washers to fit.
A drill and bit appropriate to the size of the bolts.
Stiff card (approximately 4cm × 5cm).
Squares of blotting paper.

What to do

1. Carefully measure and drill a hole in each corner of the two pieces of wood.
2. Thread the bolts through one piece of wood, using washers to protect the wood.
3. Lay a piece of card and blotting paper on the wooden base and carefully arrange the plant or flower to be pressed.
4. Cover the specimen with a piece of blotting paper and another piece of card.
5. Continue making layers of specimens in this way.
6. Place the second piece of wood on top and tighten the bolts as much as possible, using the fly nuts on the bolts and more washers to protect the wood.
7. After two or three weeks, take off the top piece of wood and look at your specimens. Mount the specimens if they have dried. They will be quite fragile and will need handling with care.
8. Laminate your specimens to make them stronger. They are best kept in a book to protect them from the light.

KEEPING WARM

Content and skills

This chapter links to Unit 4C 'Keeping warm' of the QCA Scheme of Work for science at Key Stage 2. The Keeping Warm Resource Gallery on the CD-ROM, together with the teacher's notes and photocopiable pages in this chapter, can be used when teaching this unit.

As with Unit 4C of the QCA Scheme of Work, children are helped to understand the concepts of heat and cold. The activities will help them to identify materials that are good thermal insulators and to think about the ways in which these materials are used in everyday life. The children are asked to measure temperature, and will learn that things cool down or warm up to the temperature of their surroundings. For example, hot water and iced water left in the classroom will cool down or warm up to room temperature.

The accompanying teacher's notes in this book include ways of using the resources with the whole class, for group work or with individual children. Some of the activities suggested will link with other areas of the curriculum such as maths, art, English or history. Wherever possible the activities encourage the children to ask questions and develop an enquiring approach to their learning.

Resources on the CD-ROM

The CD-ROM contains pictures of ways of keeping things hot or cold, such as a thermos flask, a fridge-freezer, an electric fan, a fishing boat with ice, a saucepan with food cooking, a child in full winter gear, baby chicks under a warming lamp and a hot water tank with an insulating jacket.

Looking at these images leads to discussions and activities on insulation as a means of keeping things hot or cold, and looking at everyday uses of insulation. Ways of devising fair tests and investigating further are also suggested.

Photocopiable pages

The photocopiable pages in the book are also provided in PDF format on the CD-ROM and can be printed out from there. They include:
▶ word cards containing essential vocabulary
▶ information sheets
▶ activity sheets.

Science and literacy skills

Skills such as observing, questioning, finding out, describing, sorting, sequencing, listening, speaking, reading, writing and drawing are needed for the activities suggested in the teacher's notes. For example, the children will: discuss ways of keeping things hot or cold and the reasons why we might need to do so; find out (by means of their own fair test) which material is best for keeping liquids hot or cold; write to a loft and cavity wall insulation firm to find out about the benefits of insulation and how effective it is.

NOTES ON THE CD-ROM RESOURCES

COOL IT!

Thermos flask, Fridge-freezer, Electric fan, Fishing boat with ice in hold

Children need to understand that certain things need to be frozen or kept cold in order to delay or stop the action of micro-organisms that make them go bad, and so to keep them fresh for longer. Micro-organisms reproduce more quickly in warm conditions. Commercially freezing and chilling goods ensures that they stay fresh longer and allows food to be transported around the world. However, there are also some things that simply taste better when cold – drinks, ice cream and so on. Children also need to investigate how things are kept cold. As well as understanding the more obvious methods of refrigeration, fans and the use of ice, they need to understand that insulation can keep things cold as well as hot. Materials that have many tiny air spaces make good insulators, because air is not a good conductor of heat and thus the air trapped around an object helps to keep the object warm or cold.

Discussing the photographs

▶ Look at each of the photographs in turn and ask the children to identify the objects in them.

▶ Can the children explain what the common link between the photographs is? (Ways to keep things cool or frozen.)

▶ Show the children the photograph of the 'Thermos flask' and talk with them about why this object is different. (Because it can keep things either hot or cold. It will keep a cold drink cold, and will also keep hot soup hot.)

▶ Ask the children why they think we need to keep things cool or frozen. For example, keeping food cold or frozen keeps it edible for longer. Explain how freezers and cold counters in shops keep the stock in good condition for longer, so that it can be offered to customers for a longer time and does not have to be replaced as quickly. Explain how keeping food cold also helps to keep it safer for us to eat by delaying the growth of potentially harmful micro-organisms.

▶ Discuss the advantages of being able to keep things cool or frozen as they are transported around the world. Explain that this enables us to import food from a long way away that would otherwise go off. For example, we import frozen lamb from New Zealand and chilled fresh fruit, such as bananas, from all over the world.

▶ Talk about the fact that some things are just nicer cold, such as ice cream and ice lollies, and that drinks can be nice in the summer with ice cubes in them.

▶ Talk about what happened before refrigerators and freezers were invented. For example, people used icehouses that they filled with ice during the winter, hoping that the ice would last through until the next winter. Explain how people made fortunes cutting ice in places like North America and Canada, then shipping it all over the world, even to places like Hong Kong. In England, we imported ice from Scandinavia to put into our icehouses until the early 20th century.

▶ Tell the children that before fridges were in common use, people used larders that had stone shelves to keep things cool. Explain that stone is a naturally cold material and in shade remains cool. Explain how these shelves were in a separate room off the kitchen. Perishable goods, such as butter or milk, would be kept on them.

▶ Discuss the fact that food is often dried or tinned to preserve it and keep it edible. Can the children think of any foods they eat that are stored in tins or dried?

▶ Look at the photograph 'Fishing boat with ice' and ask the children why they think the fish are in boxes full of ice. Talk about how putting ice in the holds of fishing boats means that the boats can fish away from land for longer periods, so that the fishermen can catch more fish without their catches going off.

▶ Ask the children how they think ice works to keep goods fresh. (It keeps things cold so that harmful bacteria cannot multiply as quickly.)

▶ Discuss why refrigerators need to be insulated. (So that they remain at a lower temperature than the surrounding air.)

▶ Look again at the 'Thermos flask' photograph and talk about the fact that it is a container surrounded by a vacuum. Explain how the inside cylinder has a double skin with the air between the layers removed, creating a vacuum. This insulates the contents efficiently from the outside temperature. The reflective surface on the inside of the flask helps to reflect heat back into (or back away from) the contents of the flask, helping to keep them hot or cold.

▶ Talk about how temperature is measured using a thermometer calibrated in degrees. Tell the children how we usually use the Celsius scale, with 0 being the freezing point and 100 being the boiling point of water at sea level. Children may sometimes notice that the weather forcasters sometimes give the temperature in Fahrenheit as well as Celsius. Explain that the Fahrenheit scale was used before the Celsius scale.

Activities

▶ Use the word cards on photocopiable pages 43–45 to familiarise the children with the key words for this unit, such as *thermal insulator* and *temperature*.

▶ Ask the children to list as many different uses for ice as they can think of. For example: for food preservation, for leisure pursuits such as ice skating, and so on.

▶ Read the information sheet 'Using ice' together (photocopiable page 46) and then give the children a copy of the activity sheet 'Finding out about ice' (photocopiable page 47). Let them use the Internet or other reference materials to answer the questions on the sheet.

▶ Collect a number of different materials, such as bubble wrap, sponge, aluminium foil, woollen clothing, cotton, paper, polystyrene and polythene. Ask the children to plan and carry out a fair test to see which insulation material stops an ice cube from melting for the longest time. Tell them to use a graphing package on the computer to represent their findings.

▶ Ask the children to find out which material keeps a drink in a can cold for the longest time. They should plan and carry out a fair test and represent their findings as a graph.

▶ Show the children the photograph of the thermos flask and ask them to investigate how long a thermos flask can keep water really cold. Do all thermos flasks keep things cold for the same length of time? Ask the children to devise a fair test to find out.

▶ Ask the children to find the best place for keeping an ice cube from melting. Can they plan and carry out a fair test to compare some options?

▶ Investigate with the children how much longer food will stay fresh if it is kept in the fridge. Use wrapped bread or cheese for the investigation. **Beware:** do not allow children to unwrap mouldy food; always dispose of the food in its wrapping; never use meat products.

▶ Ask the children to find out how long fishing boats can store fish in their holds, and how long they can be at sea.

KEEPING WARM

Saucepan cooking, Child in winter clothes, Chicks under warming lamp, Water tank with jacket

Children sometimes confuse heat and temperature and use the words interchangeably. Temperature is a measure of how hot or cold things are. Often children do not understand that the same materials will help to keep cold things cold and warm things warm. Materials that have many tiny air spaces make good insulators, because air is not a good conductor of heat and the air trapped around an object helps to keep the object warm or cold. Things that are not insulated will cool down or heat up to room temperature more quickly than things that are.

Discussing the photographs

▶ Look at each photograph in turn and ask the children to identify what is happening in it (not just what object is shown).

▶ Ask the children why we need to heat things up or keep them warm. For example, some foods are better cooked, and to do this heat needs to be applied in some way. Other things need to be kept warm (rather than heated) by insulating them, so that the heat does not escape into the colder air around them.

▶ Look again at the photograph 'Saucepan cooking'. Talk about how some foods need to be cooked and the various reasons for cooking them. For example, food may be cooked for hygiene, to make it taste better or to make it easier to chew and (in some cases) to digest.

▶ Explain to the children that when food is cooked in a saucepan the water is heated and the heat transfers to the food. Ask the children whether they know of other ways of cooking food, for example in an oven or on a barbeque.

▶ Look at the photograph 'Chicks under warming lamp' and ask the children why they think the chicks have been placed under the warming lamp. (In nature the mother hen would keep them warm.) Explain to the children that more chicks are raised commercially than there are mother hens to care for them, so they have to be raised artificially under warming lamps.

▶ Can the children tell you some other circumstances in which babies need to be kept warm? For example, premature babies are put in heated incubators in hospital to keep them at the correct temperature, because their own systems are not yet able to do this.

▶ Look at the photographs of the 'Child in winter clothes' and 'Water tank with jacket'. Talk about how winter clothes are usually made from thicker materials that have lots of air spaces making them good insulators. Talk about how we often wear more layers of clothing in cold weather, each layer trapping air between it and the next layer or the skin, giving further insulation. The jacket on the water tank is also made of a material that has millions of tiny air spaces. Well-insulated water tanks help to reduce the amount of energy used and therefore the amount of greenhouse gases produced, thus helping the environment.

Activities

▶ Use different thermos flasks and ask the children to find out whether they all keep liquids hot for the same length of time. Is the best thermos for keeping things hot the same as the best thermos for keeping things cool (see the activity on page 38)? Ask the children to write up their findings and give them the word cards on photocopiable pages 43–45 to help them.

▶ Gather together a variety of materials, such as bubble wrap, sponge, aluminium foil, woollen clothing, cotton, paper, polystyrene and polythene. Challenge the children to devise a fair test to find out which materials are best for keeping water hot. Ask the children to represent their findings on a graph, using the computer.

▶ Look at each material used in the activity above under a magnifier. Which has the most air spaces? Ask the children to write about why this could make the material a good insulator.

▶ Put a selection of spoons made from a variety of materials, such as metal, plastic and wood, in cans of hot water at the same temperature. Let the children feel the spoon handles at regular intervals. Talk about why the handles are hot or not. Is the material an insulator or a conductor? Discuss why saucepan handles are often made of wood or plastic and not metal.

▶ Help the children to find out the temperature of the classroom. They can leave a thermometer there and read and record the temperature at the start of the day, at midday and just before the children go home. Is the temperature the same at each reading? Is it the same at a given time every day? Why not? (Temperature may depend on the weather outside, the number of children in the room, and so on.)

▶ Put a cup of iced water and a cup of hot water, of the same size and with the same amount of water, in the classroom and measure the temperature of both. Leave the cups for several hours and then measure the temperatures again. Ask the children what they think will happen. Talk to them about why both cups will reach room temperature. What would happen if the cups were put in a colder or warmer room, or in the fridge? What would happen if they were both wrapped in an insulating material? Can the children devise a fair test to find out?

▶ Using tubs of cress, let the children find out what happens to plants when they are very cold. Put one tub in the fridge and one in the freezer (if this unit is being done in the winter, you could also put one outside). Use horticultural fleece to find out whether the plants can be kept warm enough to protect them from the cold.

▶ If possible, rear chicks in an incubator and under a warming lamp. (See the ASE publication *Be Safe!*) Give the children the 'Egg to chick checklist' (photocopiable page 48) to guide them through the process of incubating and raising chicks. Make sure that you have a good home for the chicks to go to after you have studied them.

▶ Ask the children to tell you about as many jobs and leisure activities as they can think of where the people doing them have to wear warm clothes. Make a list on the board. The children can then draw and annotate pictures of some of the people on the list and write about why they need those clothes. For example, fishermen's clothes have to be waterproof, as well as warm and windproof, so that the fishermen can do their job without getting wet and cold.

▶ Help the children to find out about ways that homes are insulated. Write to some loft insulation and cavity wall insulation firms for their brochures, so that the children can find out how efficient such insulation is. When they have read the information, ask them questions such as *How much warmer does insulation keep the houses that are insulated? How much is saved on the cost of heating bills? What other advantages are there in insulating houses well?* For example, using less fossil fuel.

▶ As a class, find out whether double glazing helps to insulate a building and keep it warm. Get information and specifications from a replacement window firm, or look it up on the Internet.

NOTES ON THE PHOTOCOPIABLE PAGES

Word cards

PAGES 43–45

These word cards contain some of the basic vocabulary for the children to use and learn when learning about 'Keeping warm'. They include:
▶ words relating to temperature
▶ words relating to warmth and cold.
Read through the words with the children. Ask which words they have heard before. Are there any words they don't understand?

Activities
▶ Spread the cards on the table and ask the children to find specific words.
▶ Use the words as a word bank to help the children label pictures or to help them with their writing.
▶ Give the children dictionaries and ask them to look up definitions for the words.

Using ice

PAGE 46

This sheet gives information on how ice is harvested for use in keeping food cool. It explains how food was kept cool in the past before fridges were in common use. It can be used in conjunction with the activity sheet 'Finding out about ice' (photocopiable page 47).

Discussing the text
▶ Remind the children of how we use fridges and freezers to keep things cold, and even use them to make ice.
▶ Talk about the fact that in the days before it was possible to make ice artificially, it was harvested from naturally frozen ponds, lakes and glaciers.

Activities
▶ Ask the children to tell you as many different ways as they can think of that ice is used in everyday life. Make a list. Pin the list up for the children to add to if they can think of any other uses for ice.
▶ Ask the children to find out more about the use of ice both today and in the past. They can use secondary sources or the Internet and write up their findings, or they could use the questions on the sheet 'Finding out about ice' to direct their research.
▶ Share what the children have found with the class. Has anyone found out anything unusual or different?
▶ Give the children a sheet of paper on which to make a note and a tally of every time they use ice, or another frozen product, in the course of a week. For example: eating food that has been frozen, putting ice into a drink or eating an ice cream. Make a graph of the children's tallies and find out which is the most/least common use of ice or freezing.

Finding out about ice

PAGE 47

This sheet can most usefully be used with the information text 'Using ice' (photocopiable page 46). The children can research the use of ice in the past (especially how it was used before refrigerators were invented) and record their findings on the sheet.

Egg to chick checklist

PAGE 48

This sheet gives instructions on how to look after newly hatched chicks if you are able to set this up in the classroom. Even if you are not able to set this up, it is a useful list to go through with the children to explain how living things need to be looked after. It can also be used in conjunction with 'Raising chicks' (photocopiable page 49).

Discussing the text

Before the eggs hatch

▶ Read through the sheet with the children and talk about the process of hatching chicks. Think together about the implications of looking after living things that depend absolutely on you and the children for their health and well being.

▶ Discuss why it is necessary to find someone to go on looking after the chicks when they can no longer be kept in the classroom.

▶ Ask the children whether they know what an incubator is. Talk about the fact that the incubator is a substitute for the mother hen who, if the eggs were being incubated naturally, would sit on them and keep them at the correct temperature as well as turning them regularly.

▶ Tell the children that keeping the eggs at the correct temperature and then keeping the chicks warm as they grow is essential. They are too small to generate sufficient heat for themselves and need the mother hen or a heat source to supply the heat they need. If they get cold, they could die.

▶ Look at the eggs with the children before putting them in the incubator, and then again every day to make sure that the incubator is functioning properly.

After the eggs hatch

▶ Talk to the children about taking care of living things. Tell them that the chicks need feeding, watering and keeping clean.

▶ Ask what the children think the needs of the chicks are. How important is warmth for the new chicks? What would happen to them if they were not kept warm enough?

▶ Show the children the chick crumbs and tell them that the chicks need to be kept supplied with these.

▶ Tell the children that the chicks need to be able to get clean water at all times. All living things need water, and can quickly dehydrate and even die if it is not available.

Activities

Before the eggs hatch

▶ Observe the eggs carefully as they hatch (hopefully some of them will hatch during the school day).

▶ Ask the children to make a note of all the things that they notice as the chicks are emerging.

▶ Help the children to hold the chicks very carefully and place them in the area where they are going to live. Make sure the children wash their hands after doing this.

After the eggs hatch

▶ Make a rota of children to look after the chicks. Explain that this will ensure that the chicks have food and clean water, and that the lamp that is keeping them warm is functioning properly. **(NOTE: The children must never touch the lamp.)**

▶ Ask the children to name the chicks and make a list of their names on the board. Can the children tell the chicks apart?

▶ Ask the children to observe the chicks closely every day and note any changes that are taking place. Let them make observational drawings of the chicks as they grow.

Raising chicks

PAGE 49

This sheet can be used if you are not able to hatch chicks in the classroom. It can also be used if you have hatched chicks, following the 'Egg to chick checklist' (photocopiable page 48) as a useful reinforcement activity.

Temperature word cards

temperature

thermometer

degrees

Celsius

Warmth and cold word cards (1)

thermal conductor

thermal insulator

room temperature

Warmth and cold word cards (2)

chilled

frozen

refrigerate

incubate

insulate

Using ice

People have enjoyed cool drinks and ice cream for hundreds of years. But before fridges and freezers were introduced to homes, items such as ice cream were a luxury. Ice cream had to be made and then eaten at once.

Before fridges and freezers became commonplace in houses in Britain in the 1930s, ice was harvested from ponds and rivers. The ice was packed into underground icehouses, and could sometimes be made to last right through the summer until the next ice harvest. It was sold in the streets of towns from a cart. It was also sold to restaurants and fishmongers so that they could keep food chilled and fresh for longer.

Many great houses and stately homes had their own icehouses, and so did some smaller family homes and large farms.

Commercial ice harvesting began in the early 19th century and soon became big business. Ice was shipped all over the world. The owners of the ice harvesting businesses made large profits. Harvesting the ice was hard, cold, back-breaking work. The ice to be cut was usually around half a metre thick. It was marked in blocks and cut out with saws. Horses were used to haul the ice to the icehouse, from where it was carted or shipped to the customers.

North American and Canadian firms harvested ice for use at home and abroad. In Britain we imported ice from Scandinavia until 1921, when we started to make ice in freezers.

Finding out about ice

Write about some of the destinations
to which ships loaded with ice sailed
in the 19th century.

_____

_____

_____

_____

_____

_____

How was ice harvested in the
19th century?

_____

_____

_____

_____

How did iceboxes work?

_____

_____

_____

_____

By what date did most houses
in Britain have a fridge or
freezer of their own?   _____

Egg to chick checklist

▶ Before incubating and raising chicks, make sure you have found someone to look after them when you are ready to pass them on.

▶ Incubate the eggs according to the instructions that come with the incubator.

▶ Prepare an area for raising the chicks in once they have hatched. An old paddling pool, or a very large cardboard box, with sides about 35cm to 40cm high is ideal. Line the pool or box with heavy duty plastic and cover the floor with sawdust or wood shavings.

▶ Use a spotlight anglepoise lamp clamped to a table and angled over the chicks for warmth. (Make sure the lamp is positioned so that the children can't go near or touch it, as the bulb gets very hot.)

▶ Make sure the chicks have clean water and chick crumbs available at all times.

▶ Clean the area out frequently and put down fresh sawdust.

▶ If possible, keep the chicks until they have begun to fledge (reach adult form), so that you can see the beginning of the change from chick to hen or cockerel.

▶ Always wash your hands after handling the chicks.

Raising chicks

▶ Draw a strip cartoon showing how to raise chicks from the egg.

▶ Write a caption under each picture to explain what is happening.

▶ Make sure you include all the things they need to grow healthy and strong.

1	**2**
3	**4**
5	**6**

SOLIDS AND LIQUIDS

Content and skills
This chapter links to Unit 4D 'Solids, liquids and how they can be separated' of the QCA Scheme of Work for science at Key Stage 2. The Solids and Liquids Resource Gallery on the CD-ROM, together with the teacher's notes and photocopiable pages in this chapter, can be used when teaching this unit.

Through this chapter, as with Unit 4D of the QCA Scheme of Work, children learn about solids, liquids and gases and how they can be separated. They also learn about everyday processes such as melting and dissolving.

The accompanying teacher's notes in this book include ways of using the resources with the whole class, for group work or with individual children. Some of the activities suggested will link with other areas of the curriculum such as maths, art or English. Wherever possible the activities encourage the children to ask questions and develop an enquiring approach to their learning.

Resources on the CD-ROM
The CD-ROM contains photographs of liquids and solids such as cooking oil, golden syrup, water, custard, a house brick, a block of wood, a pebble, a glass vase, plastic sandals and a metal fork. These will help children to understand what solids and liquids are and how they behave. There are images of 'difficult solids' for children to discuss and learn about, such as cotton wool, sand, rice and Plasticine; these behave to some extent like liquids, or appear to be compressible. Pictures of everyday processes such as dissolving, sieving and melting lead to activities designed to help children understand, for example, the difference between the two different physical processes of melting and dissolving. The photograph of molten metal being poured leads to a discussion of how the action of heat is necessary in the melting process, and an understanding that many solid substances can be melted.

Photocopiable pages
The photocopiable pages in the book are also provided in PDF format on the CD-ROM and can be printed out from there. They include:
▶ word cards with the essential vocabulary for the topic
▶ definition sheets that explain scientific concepts
▶ activity sheets
▶ a story about melting.

Science and literacy skills
Skills such as observing, questioning, describing, finding out, sorting, sequencing, listening, speaking, reading, writing and drawing are needed for the activities suggested in the teacher's notes. For example, 'finding out' skills are fostered when the children investigate the differences and similarities between solids, liquids and gases and how they behave. The children are also asked to sort words and phrases that apply to solids, liquids and gases. Discussing and finding out about the physical processes of melting and dissolving helps to develop the children's speaking and listening skills.

NOTES ON THE CD-ROM RESOURCES

LIQUIDS

Pouring cooking oil, Pouring golden syrup, Pouring water, Pouring custard

Children need to understand some of the properties of liquids, and to know that not all liquids are of the same thickness (viscosity), though they do not need to use the term 'viscosity' at this stage. Liquids find their own level and take the shape of their container (or the lower part of it). They cannot be squashed (compressed) so that they take up a smaller space. They flow sideways and down, but they cannot flow up. The rate at which liquids flow depends on how thick (viscous) they are.

Although the focus of this unit is solids and liquids, it is helpful if children can make comparisons and know some of the differences and similarities between solids, liquids and gases. Liquids and gases both flow and take the shape of their container; but liquids only flow sideways and down, finding their own level. Gases flow in all directions and fill their container. They can be compressed to take up a smaller space. (See the definitions sheet on page 62.)

Discussing the photographs
▶ Ask the children whether they can tell you what a liquid is and how it behaves.
▶ Talk about the fact that liquids flow sideways and down, that they find their own level and take the shape of their container, and that they take up the space they take up and cannot be compressed. See the definition sheet 'What are solids, liquids and gases?' (photocopiable page 62).
▶ Compare the properties of liquids with those of gases and talk about the fact that gases flow in all directions and take the shape of their container. Explain to the children that gases can be compressed.
▶ Look at each of the photographs in turn and ask the children to try to identify the liquid being poured.
▶ Ask the children to name some other liquids that are not shown in these photographs.
▶ Point out that the liquids in the photographs are of different thicknesses (viscosity), yet they are all liquids. When they are poured they all flow in the same way, but not necessarily at the same rate, depending on their thickness (viscosity).
▶ Talk about the fact that most substances can exist as a solid, a liquid and a gas. For example, though water is a liquid at room temperature, when it is frozen it becomes a solid (ice) and when it is heated it turns into a gas (steam).

Activities
▶ Spill different liquids onto a tray and let the children watch what happens. Do the liquids all behave in the same way even when they are of different thicknesses? Try water, syrup, tomato juice and so on.
▶ Pour water from one container to another and ask the children to focus on how it finds its own level and takes the shape of the container.
▶ Seal some water in a large syringe. Ask the children whether they think you will be able to compress it and make it take up less room in the syringe. Use the activity sheet 'Can it be compressed?' (photocopiable page 64) and seal the syringes for the children. The children can carry out the first part of the investigation and record what happens on the sheet.
▶ Drop lumps of Plasticine of the same size and shape into measuring cylinders containing the same amount of water, cooking oil, syrup and washing-up liquid. Ask the children to note what happens. Do the lumps of Plasticine fall at the same rate in each liquid? (The viscosity of the liquid makes a difference.)
▶ Ask the children to write a definition of a liquid. Use the definition sheet 'What are solids, liquids and gases?' (photocopiable page 62) if appropriate.
▶ Give the children the activity sheet 'Sort it out!' (photocopiable page 63) and ask them to identify the words and phrases that can be used to describe a liquid. (The words *light* and *heavy* have been included on the sheet – you may wish to explain to the children that most gases can be said to be 'light' relative to solids and liquids.)

▶ Compare a liquid such as Silly Putty with a solid such as Blu-Tack. Talk with the children about how these look and feel similar, but if they are rolled into a ball and placed in a small container the Blu-Tack will stay in its place whereas the Silly Putty will eventually flow sideways and down and take the shape of the container.

SOLIDS

House brick, Wood, Glass vase, Pebble, Plastic sandals, Metal fork

Children will probably not have too much difficulty identifying the objects shown in these photographs as solids. However, they do need to understand some of the properties of solids. Solids retain their shape unless a force acts on them. Although their shape may be changed by applying a force, they cannot be compressed to take up a smaller space. Solids such as Plasticine or play dough can be changed in shape relatively easily, but not without applying a force.

Discussing the photographs
▶ Ask the children to tell you what a solid is, what it does and how it behaves.
▶ Look at each of the photographs of objects. They are all solids and will retain their shapes unless a force acts upon them. The house brick can be cut or shattered, as can the glass vase. Wood can be carved and sometimes bent. A pebble can be scratched or broken. Plastic sandals are flexible, and a metal fork can be bent. None of these can be compressed to take up a smaller space.
▶ Talk to the children about how solids, like liquids, take up the space that they take up and cannot be compressed.
▶ Some solids, such as metals or chocolate, may become liquid if they are heated, but when they are allowed to cool they solidify again.

Activities
▶ Ask the children to write a definition of a solid. Let them use 'What are solids, liquids and gases?' (photocopiable page 62) if appropriate.
▶ Seal a flexible solid such as Plasticine in a large syringe and try to compress it into a smaller space. Do the same with a liquid such as water, and with a gas such as air. Write down what happens on the board and ask the children which substances can be compressed and which cannot. Let the children complete the sheet 'Can it be compressed?' (photocopiable page 64) to continue their investigation into compressing liquids, solids and gases.
▶ Put some water into a measuring cylinder and drop a ball of Plasticine into it. Measure how far the water rises (the displacement). Change the shape of the Plasticine in as many ways as possible, and drop it into the liquid each time. Is the displacement always the same? Why? (Although the shape of the plasticine has changed, the amount of material in it and the space it takes up has not, so it displaces the same amount of water.)
▶ Give the children a copy of the definition sheet 'What are solids, liquids and gases?' (photocopiable page 62). Ask them to compare a solid such as a block of wood with a liquid such as water, referring to the sheet when doing so.
▶ Give the children a copy of 'Sort it out!' (photocopiable page 63) and ask them to sort out the words and phrases that can be used to describe solids. (The words *light* and *heavy* have been included on the sheet – you may wish to explain to the children that most solids can be said to be 'heavy' relative to gases and liquids.)
▶ Compare a gas such as air with a solid and a liquid. Ask the children how it is different from these. Is it the same in any way? Ask them to write a definition of a gas, letting them use the sheet 'What are solids, liquids and gases?' (photocopiable page 62) if necessary.

'DIFFICULT' SOLIDS

Cotton wool, Heap of sand, Heap of rice, Plasticine

Some solids containing very small particles often behave like liquids in some ways. For example, sand can be poured like a liquid, and it will take the shape of any container into which it is poured. However, when it is poured onto a flat surface it will form a heap rather than flow sideways and down as a liquid would. This is because each particle that makes

up sand is a solid. Rice behaves in much the same way as sand, each grain being a solid. Powder, while behaving in some ways like a liquid, is a solid with very fine particles.

Cotton wool is a solid that behaves as if it can be compressed. The solid itself is composed of many fine filaments that cannot be compressed. When cotton wool is squeezed or squashed, the air is being squeezed out and the filaments of the cotton wool are pushed together, appearing to take up a smaller space. Plasticine can be changed in shape quite easily, but not compressed to take up a smaller space.

Discussing the photographs

▶ Show the children each photograph in turn. Talk about the fact that some solids may look as if they are behaving like gases. For example, it appears that cotton wool can be squeezed (compressed). Ask the children why they think that is the case. (It is really the air being squeezed out, not the actual solid being compressed.)

▶ Look at the photographs 'Heap of sand' and 'Heap of rice' and talk about how, although these materials are solids, they behave like liquids in some ways. For example, they can be poured. However, we know that they are solids because they make a heap and do not flow to take on the shape of the container.

▶ Look at the photograph of Plasticine and talk about it being a solid because it will stay in its place and not flow; but unlike a block of wood, it can easily be made to change shape.

Activities

▶ Make a collection of porous solids such as cotton wool and sponges, and let the children squeeze them. Discuss the idea that the air is being squeezed out of them and that the solid itself is not really being compressed.

▶ Pour sand and water into deep trays. If possible, borrow a toy water/sand wheel from a Key Stage 1 class and pour first sand and then water through it into two separate trays. List similarities and differences between how the two substances behave. How do the children know that one is a liquid and one a pourable solid? (The water flows sideways and down and takes the shape of its container. The sand flows down and piles up in the tray.)

▶ Ask the children to think of other solids that behave like liquids, such as sugar, salt, flour and coffee grounds. Let the children handle some of these carefully and see how they behave. Remind them to wash their hands afterwards, and make sure that they do not eat any of the solids.

EVERYDAY PROCESSES

Dunking a teabag, Dissolving salt, Melting fat, Dissolving ice cubes, Sifting flour, Candle melting, Chocolate melting

The photographs showing 'everyday processes' help the children to relate scientific descriptions of physical processes to everyday life. They may not associate activities such as dunking a teabag or melting chocolate with scientific terms. Melting and dissolving are often confused by both children and adults, and the words are used interchangeably. Scientifically they are very different processes. If something melts it changes from a solid to a liquid. Melting only involves one substance, which needs to be heated in order to bring about the change. Once the solid has been melted, it can be changed back into a solid by cooling. If something dissolves, this usually involves a solid being added to a liquid. It means that two or more things are mixed together. The process does not require heat and cannot be changed back by cooling. Many substances can be both melted and dissolved. For example, sugar can be melted by heating (as in the making of caramel), or dissolved (for instance, by adding it to a cup of tea). Adding sugar to a hot liquid such as tea does not melt the sugar, it just speeds up the rate at which the sugar dissolves.

Some solids that are put into a liquid do not dissolve. The 'bits' remain floating in the liquid and the mixture is not clear. For example, flour stirred into water does not dissolve but makes the water look cloudy. This is called a *suspension*. At this stage the children do not need to learn the terms *solution* and *suspension*, but you may wish to use these words with them.

Sifting flour shows the tiny particles and demonstrates how flour can flow rather as a liquid does. Salt is a substance that disappears when it is dissolved – but the water will taste of salt, showing that it is still present. Putting a teabag into water shows that a solid

can partially dissolve and sometimes change the colour of the liquid. Ice, a candle, fat and chocolate melting show how some substances, if heated, can change state from a solid to a liquid but will solidify again as they cool. Candle wax and fat also become clear as they melt and opaque again as they solidify.

Discussing the photographs

▶ Look at the photographs, one by one, and talk about what is happening in each (see above).

▶ Talk with the children about the definitions of, and the difference between, melting and dissolving. Then look at each photograph in turn with the children. Can they tell you which process is happening in each photograph and how they know? For instance, the salt dissolves; the tea partly dissolves out of the tea leaves; the fat, the candle wax and the chocolate all melt.

▶ Now look at the photograph 'Sifting flour' again. Can the children see the particles? They look rather like the particles in salt or sugar; but unlike them, flour does not dissolve. If it is mixed with water, the tiny particles float about and turn the water cloudy. This is called a *suspension*. If the mixture is set aside for long enough, the flour particles will sink to the bottom and form a layer.

▶ Ask the children to give you other examples of both melting and dissolving and to name some substances that can be either melted or dissolved, such as sugar.

▶ Discuss the fact that when one substance is dissolved in another they are totally mixed, and this is called a *solution*. Explain how the mixture is clear and contains no visible 'bits' or particles, though it may have changed colour. For example, when brown sugar is dissolved in water the resulting solution is brown but still completely clear. Adding heat only speeds up the dissolving process, but is essential for the melting process.

▶ Talk about how a substance dissolved in a liquid can be recovered by evaporating the liquid, but that there are other ways of separating mixtures. Can the children tell you any of them? For example, sieving or using a magnet to separate certain metals from other solids.

▶ Explain to the children how melting usually only involves one solid substance being heated or warmed until it liquefies. For example, ice cream melting on a hot day or ice melting in a warm room. Point out that heat is essential to melt chocolate.

▶ Tell the children that if substances that have been melted, such as chocolate, are allowed to cool they will solidify again; but where substances have been dissolved, the liquid has to be evaporated from them in order to get them back.

Activities

▶ Give the children a copy of the information sheet 'Melting and dissolving' (photocopiable page 65). This will help them to understand the differences between the two processes.

▶ Ask the children to write brief definitions of melting and dissolving to reinforce their understanding of the processes. They could use the word cards on photocopiable pages 59–61 to help them if appropriate.

▶ Give the children a copy of the activity sheet 'Melt or dissolve?' (photocopiable page 66) and ask them to decide whether each of the processes listed involves melting or dissolving.

▶ Make a collection of some substances that dissolve and others that do not dissolve when added to water. Show these to the children and ask them to predict whether the substances will dissolve or not. Then let them test the substances using a clear plastic glass or beaker. To test whether the substance is dissolved, they can place the beaker on the word *dissolved* written in black on a piece of paper. Demonstrate this. If the word can be read easily and the mixture is completely clear, then the substance is dissolved and there are no particles in suspension.

▶ Demonstrate to the children how to dissolve some salt in water and then evaporate the water in order to get the salt back. Leaving a saucer of salty water in the sun or on a radiator is a good way of doing this. (If you are evaporating the water in a saucepan on the cooker, be careful not to evaporate it completely as the hot salt tends to spit.)

▶ As a class, dissolve some other substances such as instant coffee granules or sugar; then use evaporation to get them back.

▶ Melt some substances such as chocolate, sugar and butter and then allow them to solidify again. Make sure the children understand that melting is the action of heat on a single solid substance, and that dissolving is the process of adding a solid substance to a liquid into which it disappears.

▶ Mix a range of materials together in water (for example: sugar, sand, wood shavings, tea leaves, small metal washers), and ask the children to devise a way of separating them. Provide any equipment that they might need. (The wood shavings can be scooped off using a slotted spoon, the sand and tea leaves recovered with different-sized sieves, the metal washers recovered with a magnet and the sugar recovered by evaporation.)

▶ Make a collection of different sugars, such as demerara, granulated and castor sugar. Ask the children to predict which will dissolve the quickest and devise a fair test to find out. Icing sugar can be added to the range of sugars to be dissolved, and many children will predict that it will dissolve the quickest because of its smaller particles. However, icing sugar also contains cornflour, which does not dissolve and remains in suspension, so the icing sugar and water mixture is not completely clear.

HEATING, MELTING

Molten steel

Steel is an alloy (mixture) of different metals, including iron. It is a material that is used to make things as diverse as cutlery and ships. It is strong and durable, and can easily be shaped when it is molten (melted) by pouring it into moulds. Being liquid, it will find its own level and take the shape of its container. As it cools it solidifies again, but in the new shape.

Discussing the photograph

▶ Ask the children to look carefully at the photograph and to talk about what is happening. Explain that the man is pouring steel that has been melted (is molten).

▶ Explain to the children that heating is necessary to melt and liquefy many of the substances used in everyday life. For example, metals are usually melted in order to make them into artefacts. The metal is made liquid through the action of intense heat and poured into a mould. The melted (molten) metal is then allowed to cool and solidify again, having flowed into and taken the shape of its container while it was a liquid. Explain that while cooling it can be further changed in shape by being drawn out into a wire or pressed into a flat sheet.

▶ Can the children tell you any other substances that are melted in order to make artefacts from them? For example, glass and plastic.

Activities

▶ Tell the children that steel is a mixture of metals. Ask them to find out what metals steel is made from, and to write about the steel-making process. They can carry out their research using reference books, CD-ROMs or the Internet.

▶ Ask the children to find out and list some of the things that steel is used for in everyday life.

▶ Ask the children to find out what substances glass contains, and to find out about the glass-making process. Is it similar to the steel-making process?

▶ Melt chocolate in the classroom. Ask the children to watch and describe what is happening as it melts. Pour the chocolate onto the back of a large spoon, or use simple moulds, and show the children how it changes back into a solid after taking the shape of the mould.

▶ Use a knife or large grater to scrape wax crayon onto greaseproof paper. Put another layer of greaseproof paper over the top and heat with a warm iron to make colourful designs. These can then be hung on the windows of the classroom. (Make sure the children are closely supervised when using the iron and that the iron is not too hot.)

▶ Let the children draw designs onto fabric and then show them how to fill in some areas with melted wax. They can then dip this into coloured dyes to produce colourful batik designs (the areas covered by wax will not take the dye).

▶ Read the class the story of Daedalus and Icarus (photocopiable page 67) to reinforce the idea that substances such as wax melt when subjected to heat.

NOTES ON THE PHOTOCOPIABLE PAGES

Word cards
PAGES 59–61

These word cards contain some of the basic vocabulary for the children to use and learn when learning about 'Solids, liquids and how they can be separated'. They include:
▶ words relating to states of matter
▶ words relating to separation.
Read through the word cards with the children to familiarise them with the key words of the topic. Check whether there are any words they don't understand and discuss these.

Activities
▶ Use the words as a word bank to help the children label pictures or to help them with their writing.
▶ Read some of the words, such as *solid*, *liquid*, *gas*, *melt* and *dissolve*, to the children and ask them to write down a definition of each.
▶ Use the words and their definitions to make a glossary for this unit.

What are solids, liquids and gases?
PAGE 62

This sheet provides definitions of a solid, a liquid and a gas.

Discussing the text
▶ Read out the definition of a solid to the class without mentioning what you are describing, and ask the children to tell you whether you are talking about a solid, a liquid or a gas.
▶ Repeat the process by reading out the definitions of a liquid and a gas.
▶ Name a solid, a liquid and a gas and ask the children to describe their properties for you.

Activities
▶ Ask the children to write a leaflet for younger children that will help them to understand the similarities and differences between solids, liquids and gases.

Sort it out!
PAGE 63

This sheet provides a series of words and phrases about the properties of solids, liquids and gases for the children to sort.

Discussing the text
▶ Ask the children to remind you of some of the properties of solids, liquids and gases that they have been learning about.
▶ Are any of the properties the same for more than one type of substance? For example, being impossible to compress.

Activities
▶ Give the children a copy of the sheet and ask them to colour the words that describe the properties of a solid red, those that describe the properties of a liquid blue and those that describe the properties of a gas green. Are any of the words multi-coloured now?
▶ Ask the children to cut out the words on the sheet and sort them into three sets: one for solids, one for liquids and one for gases. Go through the sets of words with the children. Were they correct? Can some words be sorted more than one way?

Can it be compressed?
PAGE 64

This sheet gives instructions to the children to help them carry out a simple investigation to find out whether a solid, a liquid and a gas can be compressed by sealing each substance in a syringe. This reinforces the children's understanding that solids and liquids cannot be compressed but gases can.

Ask the children to remind you of the similarities and differences between solids, liquids and gases that they have been learning about. Tell them that the investigation they are about

to do demonstrates one similarity between solids and liquids and how gases are different. Look at the sheet with the children and make sure that they understand it. When they have completed the investigation, ask the children to tell you what they found out. Were they able to compress all three materials? Which one was different?

Melting and dissolving

PAGE 65

This sheet provides definitions of the processes of melting and dissolving.

Discussing the text

▶ Ask the children to remind you what they have learned about melting and dissolving. Can they tell you the difference between the two processes?

▶ Tell them that the two processes are very different in scientific terms, but that they are often confused, even by adults.

Activities

▶ Give the children a copy of the sheet and ask them to read through it. Talk about the difference between the two processes.

▶ Ask the children to write their own definitions of melting and dissolving. They could use the word cards on photocopiable pages 59–61 to help them if necessary.

Melt or dissolve?

PAGE 66

This is a sheet to test the children's understanding of melting and dissolving. They need to decide which process is happening in each of the situations listed, and to add their own example of each process.

Daedalus and Icarus

PAGE 67 AND PAGE 68

This is the story, retold from Greek mythology, of how Icarus flew too near to the Sun and melted the wax holding his wings together. This story reinforces the concept that some materials melt when they are heated.

Discussing the text

Ask the children to read the story, or read it aloud to the class.

▶ Tell the children that the story comes from Greek mythology and is thousands of years old.

▶ Ask the children to tell you why Icarus's wings failed as he got nearer the Sun. Was wax a sensible material to use? (It was easy to stick the feathers into, but Icarus should not have gone too near a source of heat.)

▶ Reinforce the definition of melting with the children and ask them to tell you how it is different from dissolving.

Activities

▶ Ask the children to read the story again to themselves.

▶ Get the children to write their own story involving the melting process.

▶ Ask the children to make a collection of substances that melt, such as wax, chocolate, butter and so on; melt them, observing closely what happens; then allow them to solidify again and observe what happens.

States of matter word cards (1)

solid

liquid

gas

melt

freeze

States of matter word cards (2)

runniness

particle

solidify

take the shape of

Separation word cards

dissolve

solution

filter

undissolved

Solid

Keeps its shape

Stays in place

Cannot be compressed

Hard

Relatively heavy (dense)

Liquid

Finds its own level

Takes the shape of its container

Fluid and runny

Flows downwards

Cannot be compressed

Relatively heavy (dense)

Gas

Completely fills its container

Invisible/transparent

Flows in all directions

Can be compressed

Relatively light (not dense)

Sort it out!

Light

Fluid

Can be compressed

No fixed shape

Runny

Invisible

Cannot be compressed

Stays in place

Does not change shape

Firm

Spreads everywhere

Hard

Flows

Fixed shape

Dry

Squashy

Stays still

Can flow up

Pours sideways or down

Soft

Heavy

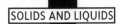

Can it be compressed?

Take three large plastic syringes. Fill one syringe with water. Ask your teacher to seal the needle end by heating with a match or candle.

Try to compress the substance by pressing down the plunger. Write what happens.

_____

_____

_____

Fill another syringe with a solid. A cylinder of Plasticine or a piece of dowel of the right diameter will do. Put the plunger back. Ask your teacher to seal the needle end by heating with a match or candle.

Try to compress the substance by pressing down the plunger. Write what happens.

_____

_____

_____

Leave the third syringe with air in it. Put the plunger back. Ask your teacher to seal the needle end by heating with a match or candle.

Try to compress the air by pressing down the plunger. Write what happens.

_____

_____

_____

Melting or dissolving

Melting

If something melts it:
- ▶ changes from a solid to a liquid
- ▶ only involves one substance
- ▶ needs to be heated
- ▶ can be changed back into a solid by cooling.

Dissolving

If something dissolves it:
- ▶ usually involves a solid being added to a liquid
- ▶ means two or more things mixing
- ▶ does not need heat
- ▶ cannot be changed back by cooling.

Many substances, such as sugar, can be melted by heating. That is what happens to sugar when caramel is made.

Many substances can be dissolved. That is what happens when sugar is added to water. If the liquid is hot, as when sugar is added to tea, the heat does not melt the sugar: it just speeds up the rate at which the sugar dissolves.

Melt or dissolve?

Tick the process that is taking place.

	Melt	Dissolve
Putting bath salts into a bath		
Heating sugar in a saucepan		
Placing ice out in the sunshine		
Making coffee with instant coffee powder		
Adding sugar to water		
Heating chocolate for a cake topping		
Putting sugar into tea		
Leaving an ice lolly in the sunshine		
Defrosting the fridge		
An ice cream on a hot day		
Holding chocolate in the hand		
Adding salt to water		

Add one more example of melting and one of dissolving to the table.

What happens to the dissolving process if hot water is used instead of cold water?

_____

_____

_____

_____

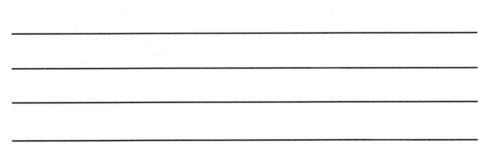

SCHOLASTIC
PHOTOCOPIABLE

Daedalus and Icarus

Daedalus was a wonderful builder and craftsman in ancient times. He had a son whom he loved very much, called Icarus. Daedalus worked for mighty Minos, the king of Crete. He built the famous labyrinth, a great maze of winding underground passages, in the rock under the King's palace. In that labyrinth King Minos kept a ferocious beast, the Minotaur, half man and half bull, who terrorised anyone who ventured into the labyrinth. (But that is another story!)

King Minos was very fierce and warlike and easily angered. One day, Daedalus made him so angry that he feared for his life and that of his son Icarus. King Minos forbade them to leave until he had decided on a punishment. Crete, of course, is an island (you can look for it on a map), and in those days it was impossible to leave without the permission of the King, whose spies were everywhere. No ship could set sail without him knowing.

Daedalus was beside himself with worry and fear, not just for himself but also for his son. He paced up and down, trying to find a way of escaping the terrible anger of the King.

"As there is no way to get off the island by boat," he thought, "we must fly." Calling for a fire to be built, he began to put his plan into effect. He called for wax and many feathers. He melted the wax over the fire, left it to cool until it was nearly hard again and then fixed feathers into it in the shape of four great wings. He made two wings for himself and two for his son. The wax that was left over he used to bond the wings to their shoulders so that they could fly. They were to fly to nearby Sicily, where Daedalus knew that they would be welcome.

Standing on the cliffs on the edge of the island of Crete, they both took to the air. Icarus was frightened and flew very timidly at first. His father encouraged him, and gradually he became more

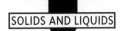

Daedalus and Icarus

and more confident and began to climb. He swooped and dived, showing off and enjoying the freedom and the rush and swoop of flying. They sped over the sea. Daedalus smiled to himself when he thought of the fury and rage of King Minos when he found that they had escaped him.

He was so busy thinking of his triumph that he forgot to keep an eye on Icarus. Icarus was getting more and more daring as he got used to flying and began to climb towards the Sun. He liked feeling its wonderful warmth on his skin. Higher and higher he went, spiralling upwards, until when Daedalus looked for him he was just a speck in the distance. Daedalus realised the danger his son was in.

"Come down, come down, Icarus, remember the wax!" Daedalus shouted.

Icarus began to feel the wax softening and melting in the heat. He realised that the wax held the wings to his shoulders and kept the feathers in place. He tried to plunge down through the air away from the hot Sun, but it was too late. The beautiful wings that had enabled him to fly like a bird began to come apart and fall from his shoulders. As they fell Icarus fell too, and he plummeted into the sea. His body was swept far away by the waves.

Daedalus landed safely in Sicily, his triumph turned to grief and despair. Though he lived a long life, he never got over the tragedy of losing his beloved son. He could not forgive himself for not warning Icarus that wax melts when it is heated, and that he should not fly too near the Sun.

READY RESOURCES ▶▶ S C I E N C E

■ SCHOLASTIC
PHOTOCOPIABLE

CIRCUITS AND CONDUCTORS

Content and skills

This chapter links to Unit 4F 'Circuits and conductors' of the QCA Scheme of Work for science at Key Stage 2. The Circuits and Conductors Resource Gallery on the CD-ROM, together with the teacher's notes and photocopiable pages in this chapter, can be used when teaching this unit of work.

Through this chapter, as with Unit 4F of the QCA Scheme of Work, children learn about simple circuits and switches and some of the dangers of electricity.

The accompanying teacher's notes in the book include ways of using the resources with the whole class, for group work or with individual children. Some of the activities suggested will link with other areas of the curriculum such as maths, art or English. Wherever possible the activities encourage the children to ask questions and develop an enquiring approach to their learning.

Resources on the CD-ROM

The CD-ROM contains diagrams of electrical circuits to help children revise what they have learned in Year 2 about the need for a complete circuit. The children can look at each circuit and predict what will happen, then make the circuits and test their predictions. A sheet of symbols is provided to help the children use symbols instead of representational drawings in their circuit diagrams. There are photographs of some electrical connectors (plugs and leads) that the children may be familiar with, together with photographs of three different types of switch.

Photocopiable pages

The photocopiable pages in the book are also provided in PDF format on the CD-ROM and can be printed out from there. They include:
▶ word cards with the essential vocabulary for the topic
▶ an instruction sheet for making and using a 'Steady hand' electrical game
▶ an information sheet showing how to make four different types of switch
▶ a picture illustrating some of the dangers of misusing electrical appliances.

Science and literacy skills

Skills such as observing, questioning, describing, finding out, sorting, sequencing, listening, speaking, reading, writing and drawing are needed for the activities suggested in the teacher's notes. For example, making simple switches will help children to find out about conductors and insulators and how they can be used to affect the flow of electricity. Making circuits or finding out why a circuit does not work will help children to think logically and hone their skills of observation.

NOTES ON THE CD-ROM RESOURCES

Wiring diagrams

Children do not always appreciate that all devices that use electricity as an energy source must have a complete circuit in order to work. This applies to the lighting in a house and the operation of a computer or a washing machine, as well as the simple circuits the children can make with bulbs and batteries.

At this stage, the children need to learn that the components in a circuit need to be of the same voltage, and know the likely results if they are not. For example, a 1.5V bulb put into a circuit using a 4.5V battery will burn out, while a 6V bulb will be dimmer than it should be. A buzzer needing a 6V supply may fail to work with a lower voltage. A 6V motor will turn slowly if used with a 4.5V battery, and even more slowly if used with a 1.5V cell.

SAFETY: Never use rechargeable batteries for circuit work. A fully-charged battery can produce a great deal of heat if short-circuited, enough to burn a child.

Discussing the illustration

▶ Look at the circuits and remind the children that a complete circuit is necessary for a device to work.

▶ Explain that the energy source, whether a battery or the mains supply, is a necessary part of the circuit.

▶ Look at the circuits again and ask the children to predict which circuits will work and which will not. Can they explain why? Circuits A and B will work; in circuit C the switch is open and the circuit will therefore not work. Circuits D and E are complete and will work. Circuit F is incorrectly wired and would, in fact, create a short circuit.

▶ Discuss the different components that could be used in a circuit and how they need to match the voltage of the energy source. Explain that a 6V buzzer may not work, and a 6V bulb will only shine dimly, if connected to a 1.5V cell. A 1.5V bulb connected to a 6V energy supply will burn out.

Activities

▶ Use the word cards on photocopiable pages 75–77 to revise some of the vocabulary used when talking about electricity.

▶ Show the children a collection of different batteries and note the voltage marked on the side of each. Remind the children that they should never take batteries apart, as this can be very dangerous. Some children may be ready to understand the difference between a battery and a cell. A single battery is more properly called a cell (usually 1.5v), while a battery is composed of two or more cells. These may be combined within a case making, for example 4.5v or 6v batteries.

▶ Let the children make the circuits in the 'Circuit illustrations'. Challenge them to think about how the circuits that don't work could be made to do so.

▶ Encourage the children to experiment with making their own circuits. They can draw and label diagrams of their circuits, using the 'Circuit illustrations' as a guide.

▶ Working in pairs, ask one child to draw a circuit and then invite their partner to decide whether it will work or not.

▶ Ask the children to redraw the circuits on the 'Circuit illustrations' using symbols instead of drawings. Give them a copy of 'Electrical symbols' (provided on the CD-ROM) to help them if necessary.

Electrical symbols

These are just a few of the symbols used in electrical diagrams. It would be unweildy to actually draw each component when designing a circuit, and the drawing would become very confusing. A series of symbols for each component has been adopted internationally, so that wiring diagrams can be understood by people who live in different countries.

Discussing the symbols

▶ Look at the symbols with the children and discuss what each symbol means. Which of these components have they used in their circuits?

▶ Talk about how these symbols are used in different countries so that people can understand diagrams even if they speak a different language.
▶ Talk about how using symbols simplifies diagrams and makes them easier to interpret.

Activities
▶ Give each child a copy of the 'Circuit illustrations' (provided on the CD-ROM) and ask the children to redraw them using the appropriate symbols.
▶ Ask the children to draw a circuit of their own design using symbols. They can then exchange drawings with a friend and collect the appropriate components to make their friend's circuit.

SWITCHES

Standard wall light switch, Button switch on a fan, Turn switch on a radio

A switch is really just a simple and convenient way of making or breaking a circuit. The actual type of switch may vary according to the device being controlled. This section helps children to understand that there are different types of switches, and to explore and make their own simple switches that can be incorporated into their own circuits or simple devices.

Discussing the pictures
▶ Ask the children to tell you about switches they use regularly – for example, to turn lights on or off, or to turn on a computer, radio or battery-operated game.
▶ Look at the photographs of the different switches. Ask the children: *Do all switches look the same?* For example, some switches are pushed (like the fan switch), some are pressed up and down (like the wall light switch) and some are turned (as on the radio).
▶ Show the children the 'Turn switch on a radio' photograph and explain how the switch controls the volume of the radio as well as turning the radio on and off. Ask whether any of the children have dimmer switches at home. Explain that these work in a similar way to the turn switch on the radio, but control the intensity of the light so that it can be varied.
▶ Discuss the fact that some materials conduct electricity very well (conductors), while others do not (insulators). These attributes of materials are used in many switches. For example, a simple pressure switch may use card (an insulator) to separate two pieces of aluminium foil (conductors). If there is a hole in the card, pressure at this point can make a connection between the two pieces of foil, thus completing the circuit and allowing the device to work.

Activities
▶ Give each child a copy of 'Switches' (photocopiable page 79) and discuss with the children how switches work by making or breaking a circuit.
▶ Let the children make the simple switches shown on the 'Switches' sheet (photocopiable page 79) and test each one in a simple circuit.
▶ Ask the children whether any of the switches on the 'Switches' sheet (photocopiable page 79) match any of the switches in the photographs. (The pressure switch is a very simple version of the button switch on the fan.) Remind the children that all switches simply complete oir break a circuit.
▶ Take the children on a walk around the school and ask them to look for examples of the switches in the photographs. Can they find them all?
▶ Make a collection of objects such as a paper clip, a piece of string, a plastic drinking straw, a cocktail stick, and so on. Ask the children to place these, one at a time, in a circuit instead of a switch and find out which materials conduct electricity. Make a list of conductors and insulators on the board.
▶ Use a pressure or tilt switch to make a burglar alarm with the children.
▶ The children could use a tilt switch to make a timing device.
▶ Give the children a copy of the 'Steady hand game' (photocopiable page 79). Help them to set the circuit up and let them play the game. Explain how the game works by making and breaking the circuit.

CONNECTIONS

Three-pin plug, Headphone connector, Extension lead, Back of computer

Most children will be familiar with different plugs, leads and sockets, and will have used them to connect various devices. However, they may not have thought about the materials used to make them or why such materials were chosen. The core of a cable or lead is usually made of metal – often many fine strands of copper twisted together to make a stronger wire. Copper, like most metals, is a good conductor and will allow electrical energy to pass easily from the mains supply to an electrical device to make it work. However, mains electricity at 230–240V has enough power to injure or even kill somebody, so the current-carrying wire needs to be shielded so that people cannot come into direct contact with 'live' wires.

Plastic is a good insulator. It does not conduct electricity, and is the material most often used these days to insulate electrical components. A flexible type of plastic is used to cover cables and leads so that they can bend around corners. A more rigid type of plastic is used for casings and components such as plugs and wall sockets.

The photograph of the three-pin plug will be familiar to most children. It shows how plastic is used for the part we hold, but the metal pins actually go into the socket to make the electrical connection. The headphone connector works in a similar way, though the plug is a different shape as it fits into a different type of socket. The extension lead shows both the flexibility of a plastic-covered metal wire and the rigid plastic used for the sockets. The back of the computer helps to illustrate some of the different types of plugs and sockets and the importance of good insulation. If any of the wires in the photograph were not insulated, the whole computer could be 'live' and very dangerous.

Discussing the photographs

▶ Look carefully at the photographs. Ask the children to identify each connector and say where it might be used.
▶ Remind the children about work they have done on insulators and conductors.
▶ Talk about the various materials used in the items in the photographs and ask the children why they think there is a mixture of metal and plastic. Ask: *Why is metal used for the pins in an electric plug? Why are the plugs themselves plastic? Why are wires sheathed in plastic?*
▶ Discuss the dangers of touching a plug that is connected to a power supply. Remind the children that the power should always be switched off before plugs are taken from sockets.

Activities

▶ Use the word cards on photocopiable page 77 to familiarise the children with terms such as electrical conductor and electrical insulator.
▶ Take a three-pin plug to pieces and discuss the various components with the class. Discuss why the wires connected to the plug are different colours. Explain that the colours of the wires are standardised throughout Europe to reduce the danger of people making the wrong connections in goods imported from other countries. The current is carried from the mains supply to the piece of equipment through a flexible lead. The live wire, coloured brown, is connected to the fused or 'live' side of the plug. The blue wire is the neutral wire, and the yellow and green striped wire is the earth wire. Equipment is earthed to prevent electric shocks in the case of something going wrong with the equipment: the electricity will flow safely into the ground through the earth wire. The equipment may still work if the wires are connected to the wrong terminals, but it may be live even when it has been switched off, and can cause shocks or fires. In Britain, all electrical appliances are sold with the plug already attached to prevent plugs being accidentally connected incorrectly.
▶ Show the children what a fuse looks like and what it does. Describe how it protects a piece of equipment by melting or burning out if too much current is applied.
▶ Ask the children to write a leaflet explaining how to wire a plug safely. They should include an explanatory diagram.

Dangers of electricity

As they are out and about, the children may see warning signs similar to those shown here. It is very important that children take notice of any such warnings, since electricity can be extremely dangerous. These sort of warnings are usually to be found on pylons, substations, railway lines and so on, where the voltage carried is often very high and could kill anyone coming into contact with it.

Discussing the signs

▶ Look at the signs with the children and ask them what sort of message they are conveying. Why do they think this? Lead them towards thinking about the words used, such as *danger* and *beware*.

▶ Stress the dangers of electricity, especially when a high voltage is present. Discuss some places that the children might know where high-voltage electricity is present, for example railway lines. Warn the children of the dangers of playing near railway lines. Explain that there is not just the danger of being run over by a train: the danger of falling onto the live rail is possibly greater.

▶ Discuss what places the signs warn of (pylons and electric fences).

▶ Talk about playing near sub-stations or pylons. Ask the children to tell you why they should not climb pylons or enter a sub-station. Tell the children it is better to lose a ball than lose their life.

▶ Talk about electric fences that are erected to keep animals in a field, or to stop them grazing on new pasture before it is ready. Explain that when farmers put up an electric fence, it has to have a sign warning people of the danger. An electric fence is unlikely to kill, but it could give a nasty shock.

▶ Discuss the dangers of using electrical equipment near water. Tell the children that water is a good conductor of electricity and that electrical equipment such as hair dryers and fan heaters should never be used in a bathroom. Explain that this is why electrical sockets, other than shaver points, are never fitted in bathrooms. Similarly, electrical equipment should never be handled with wet hands, as this creates the risk of an electric shock.

Activities

▶ Ask the children to make a poster warning about the dangers of playing near high-voltage sources.

▶ Ask the children to write a story about someone who ignored warnings about playing near high-voltage sources.

▶ With the children, mark any danger spots on a map of the local area.

▶ Give the children copies of 'Find the danger' (photocopiable page 80) to familiarise them with electrical dangers around the home.

NOTES ON THE PHOTOCOPIABLE PAGES

Word cards

PAGES 75-77

These word cards contain some of the basic vocabulary for the children to use and learn when looking at the topic of 'Circuits and conductors'. They include:

▶ words relating to circuits

▶ words relating to materials in circuits.

Read through the word cards with the children. Ask which words the children have heard before. Are there any words they don't understand?

Activities

▶ Spread the word cards on the table and ask the children to find specific words.

▶ Use the cards as a word bank to help the children label pictures or to help them with their writing.

▶ Encourage the children to look up the meaning of any unfamiliar words in a dictionary.

Steady hand game

This sheet gives instructions for making a fun electrical game. You could get the class to make it to use as a competition at the next school fête.

Discussing the text
▶ Discuss how the device on the sheet works. Talk about how the loop completes the circuit when it touches the wire shape and sounds the alarm.
▶ Talk about what would happen if the loop were made of plastic instead of metal.
▶ Remind the children that plastic is an insulator and does not conduct electricity, and therefore will not close or complete the circuit.

Activities
▶ Follow the instructions and help the children make the game.
▶ The children could try using different-shaped wires to navigate the loop around. Beginners at the game could make simple wire shapes, while experts could make more complex shapes.
▶ Invite children from another group or class to try the game.

Switches

These are simple switches that the children can make for themselves. Discuss each type of switch with the children before they begin to make the switches. Discuss what is needed and what tools will be required to make each one. Remind the children of safety issues when using tools such as awls or drills.

When the children have made the switches discuss where they might be used – for example, to control lights or motors (dimmer switch), or to activate an alarm in a simple timing device (tilt switch).

Find the danger

We are so used to electricity being part of our everyday lives that it is often not treated with the respect it needs. This picture shows a family with little regard for their own safety!

Discussing the illustration
▶ Look at the picture and ask the children to tell you any electrical hazards they can spot. For example: an overloaded socket, frayed leads, a child cutting flex, a plug hanging from a kettle near water, a man with a hedge cutter not plugged into a circuit breaker (see below).
▶ Talk about how dangerous it is to cut electrical leads or cables if they are connected to a power supply.
▶ Ask the children whether they can tell you why it is dangerous to overload a socket (it may blow a fuse and stop working, or it may overheat and cause a fire).
▶ Talk about the dangers of mixing electricity and water. Look at the appliance that has been allowed to hang in the sink. Talk about how impure water (such as tap water) is a good conductor of electricity, and it could be very dangerous if someone put their hands into the water.
▶ Discuss the dangers of leads hanging over the edges of worktops. They can easily get caught on something and the appliance pulled over, causing burns or scalds.
▶ Talk about how flexes and leads should be checked regularly and be replaced if there are signs of wear.
▶ Discuss the fact that electrical equipment used outdoors should always be plugged into a circuit breaker. This is a device that will shut off the electricity if there is any kind of fault with the equipment, keeping the operator safe from electric shock.

Activities
▶ Give each child a copy of the illustration and ask them to mark all the hazards they can see.
▶ Ask the children to write a short piece about one of the hazards, explaining why it is dangerous.

Circuit word cards (1)

battery

bulb

buzzer

motor

break

Circuit word cards (2)

switch

connection

plug

wire

cable

Circuit/material word cards

electrical conductor

electrical insulator

metal

plastic

Steady hand game

You will need:

A piece of wood 30cm long, 15cm wide and 2cm thick.

2 small cubes of wood 2cm long, thick and wide.

A wire coathanger or other piece of thick bare wire.

A small piece of dowelling wood, approximately 10cm long.

Covered wire.

A battery.

2 screw-eyes.

A buzzer or lamp (bulb).

1. Cut the hook from the coat hanger and bend the wire into a curly shape.

2. Drill holes in the two small blocks, then push in the ends of the wire and fix with a little glue.

3. Glue the blocks to the board.

4. Bend a short length of thick wire into a loop around the shaped wire.

5. Drill a hole in the centre of one end of the dowel and insert the ends of the loop to make a handle (see illustration below).

6. Glue the buzzer to the base. Screw in both screw-eyes.

7. Make connections from: **a)** one end of the wire shape to the buzzer, **b)** from the buzzer to one screw-eye, **c)** the loop to the second screw-eye (using a piece of wire approximately 45cm long).

8. Connect the battery to the screw-eyes, and you're ready to play the game.

Switches

Switch

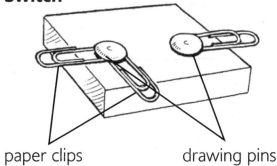

paper clips   drawing pins

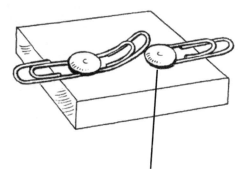

Bend paper clips up to make push down switch.

Pressure switch

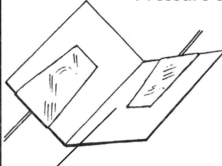

folded card

1. Fold foil over card, glue foil to card, attach bare wire to outside of foil.

2. Cut a hole in a piece of card.

foil

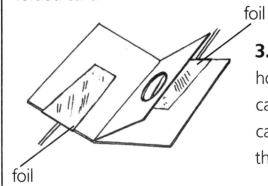

foil

3. Place card with the hole inside the folded card, so that the foil can make contact through the hole.

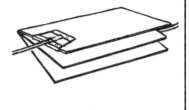

Dimmer switch

Shave the wood from one side of a BB pencil. Then slide a crocodile clip along the pencil 'lead'.

Tilt switch

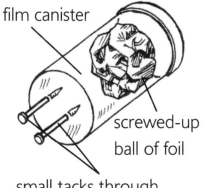

film canister

screwed-up ball of foil

small tacks through bottom of canister

Find the danger

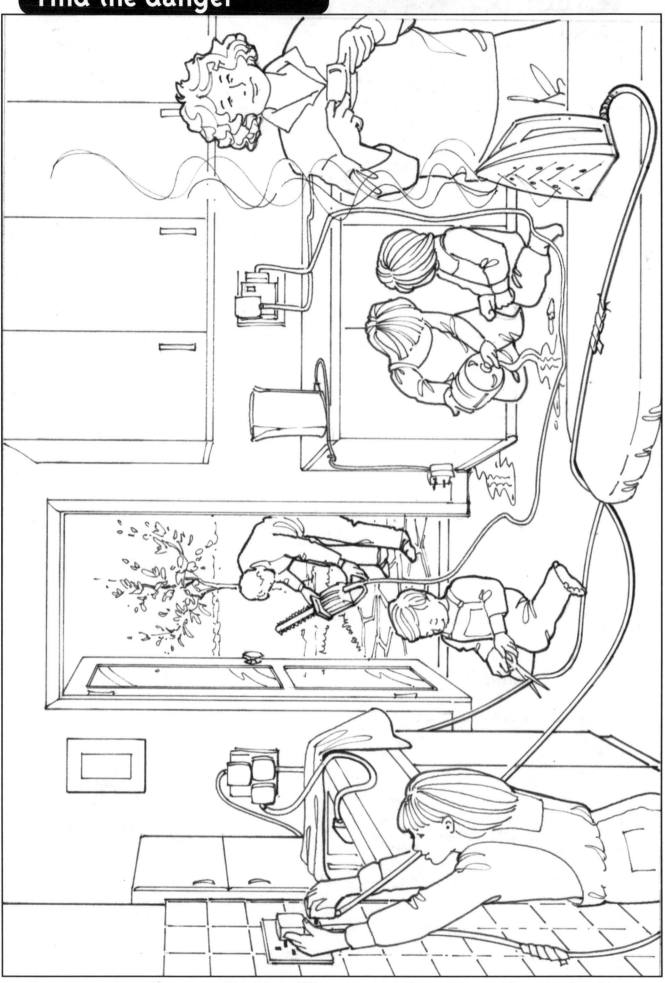